Susan Gardner

ESSENTIALS

Edexcel

INTERNATIONAL GCSE

Physics

Contents

Contents

Movement and Position

Speed

The **speed** of an object is a measure of how fast it's moving. Speed is measured in:

- metres per second (m/s)
- kilometres per hour (km/h)
- miles per hour (mph).

You can work out the speed of a moving object if you know:

- the **distance** it travels (measured using a measuring tape/trundle wheel)
- the **time it takes** to travel that distance (measured using a stopwatch/stopclock).

The faster the speed of an object:

- the greater the distance it travels in a particular time
- the shorter the time it takes to travel a particular distance.

You can calculate the speed of an object by using this formula:

Speed (m/s) $=$ **Distance travelled** (metres) / **Time taken** (s)

$$\frac{d}{s \times t}$$

The speed may change over a given distance so the average speed over the whole journey is used.

Distance = Average speed × Time taken

> **Example 1**
>
> Calculate the speed of a cyclist who travels 2400m in 5 minutes.
>
> $$\text{Speed} = \frac{\text{Distance travelled}}{\text{Time taken}}$$
>
> $$= \frac{2400\text{m}}{300\text{s}} = \textbf{8m/s}$$

You can rearrange the speed formula to calculate either distance or time taken.

> **Example 2**
>
> Calculate the distance a car travels in 90 minutes if it's travelling at a constant speed of 80km/h.
>
> $$\text{Speed} = \frac{\text{Distance travelled}}{\text{Time taken}}$$
>
> So, Distance = Speed × Time taken
>
> $$= 80\text{km/h} \times 1.5\text{h} = \textbf{120km}$$

> **Example 3**
>
> Calculate the time it takes a motorcyclist to travel a distance of 120km at 50km/h.
>
> $$\text{Time taken} = \frac{\text{Distance travelled}}{\text{Speed}}$$
>
> $$= \frac{120\text{km}}{50\text{km/h}} = 2.4 \text{ hours} = \textbf{2h 24min}$$

Experiments to Investigate Motion

You can investigate motion using a trolley, a ramp and ticker tape.

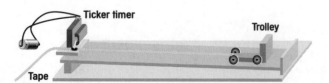

Ticker timer

Trolley

Tape

You can take measurements of time (s), distance from start (cm), distance covered in last 0.1s (cm) and therefore average speed for last 0.1s (cm/s). You can use the results to draw a distance–time graph and a velocity–time graph (see pages 5 and 7).

Distance–Time Graphs

The slope of a **distance–time graph** represents the **speed** of an object. The **steeper the gradient (slope)**, the **greater the speed**.

This graph shows the movement of three people.

1 A stationary person standing 10m from point (O).

2 A person moving at a constant speed of 2m/s.

3 A person moving at a greater constant speed of 3m/s.

4 A person moving at the same speed as **2** but in the opposite direction. This graph will have the same gradient but will slope in the opposite direction.

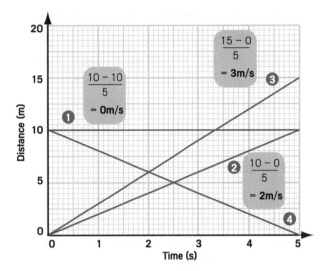

Calculating Speed

To work out the speed of an object, take any two points on a distance–time graph and read off the distance travelled for that part of the journey, and the time taken to get there (see Graph 1).

By looking at the graph, you can use the formula to calculate the speed at each part of the journey.

O to A: Speed $= \dfrac{15 - 0\text{m}}{3\text{s}} = $ **5m/s**

A to B: Speed $= \dfrac{15 - 15\text{m}}{5\text{s}} = $ **0m/s**

B to C: Speed $= \dfrac{0 - 15\text{m}}{4\text{s}} = $ **−3.75m/s**

> Negative sign shows that the object is moving in the reverse direction, i.e. back towards the starting point.

So, the object:
- travelled at 5m/s for 3 seconds
- remained stationary for 5 seconds
- travelled at 3.75m/s for 4 seconds back to the starting point.

Graphs can also be drawn for **non-uniform speed** (see Graph 2).

Graph 1 – Calculating Speed

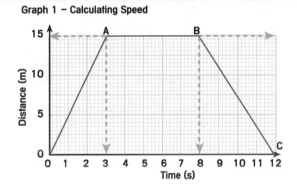

Graph 2 – Non-uniform Speed

O to A
Gradually increasing gradient shows object's speed is increasing.

A to B
Gradually decreasing gradient shows object's speed is decreasing.

Quick Test

1 What two quantities are needed to calculate speed?

2 What does the gradient of a distance–time graph represent?

3 Describe how you can investigate motion.

Movement and Position

Acceleration

The **acceleration** or **deceleration** of an object is the change in **velocity** per second. It's a measure of how quickly an object **speeds up** or **slows down**. Acceleration is **only** measured in **metres per second squared** (m/s^2). To work out the acceleration of a moving object, you need to know:

- the **change in velocity**
- the **time taken** for the change in velocity.

You can calculate the acceleration (or deceleration) of an object by using this formula:

$$\text{Acceleration } (m/s^2) = \frac{\text{Change in velocity } (m/s)}{\text{Time taken } (s)}$$

Example 1

A cyclist accelerates uniformly from rest and reaches a velocity of 10m/s after 5 seconds. He then decelerates uniformly and comes to rest in a further 10 seconds.

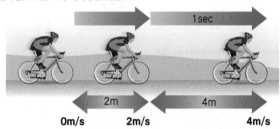

1 sec

2m   4m

0m/s   2m/s   4m/s

a) Calculate his acceleration.

$$\text{Acceleration} = \frac{\text{Change in velocity}}{\text{Time taken for change}}$$

$$= \frac{10 - 0\,m/s}{5s} = \textbf{2m/s}^2$$

b) Calculate his deceleration (negative acceleration).

$$= \frac{0 - 10\,m/s}{10s}$$

$$= \textbf{-1m/s}^2 \text{ acceleration} = \textbf{1m/s}^2 \text{ deceleration}$$

The acceleration formula can be rearranged to calculate time taken or change in velocity.

Example 2

A car accelerates at $1.5m/s^2$ for 12 seconds. Calculate the change in velocity of the car.

Change in velocity = Acceleration × Time taken
$$= 1.5m/s^2 × 12s = \textbf{18m/s}$$

Velocity–Time Graphs

The slope of a **velocity–time graph** represents the **acceleration** of the object. A constant acceleration increases the velocity.

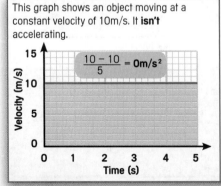

This graph shows an object moving at a constant velocity of 10m/s. It **isn't** accelerating.

$$\frac{10 - 10}{5} = 0m/s^2$$

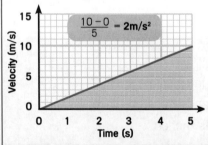

This graph shows an object moving at a constant acceleration of $2m/s^2$.

$$\frac{10 - 0}{5} = 2m/s^2$$

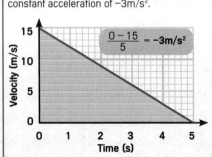

This graph shows an object moving at a constant acceleration of $-3m/s^2$.

$$\frac{0 - 15}{5} = -3m/s^2$$

Velocity–Time Graphs (Cont.)

To work out the acceleration of an object, take any two points on a velocity–time graph. Read off the change in velocity over the chosen period and the time taken for this change.

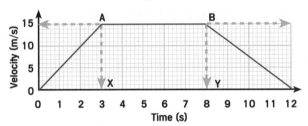

You can use the acceleration formula to calculate the acceleration at each part of the journey.

O to A: Acceleration $= \dfrac{15\text{m/s} - 0\text{m/s}}{3\text{s}} = \mathbf{5\text{m/s}^2}$

A to B: Acceleration $= \dfrac{15\text{m/s} - 15\text{m/s}}{5\text{s}} = \mathbf{0\text{m/s}^2}$

B to C: Acceleration $= \dfrac{0\text{m/s} - 15\text{m/s}}{4\text{s}} = \mathbf{-3.75\text{m/s}^2}$

So, the object:

- accelerated at 5m/s² for 3 seconds
- travelled at a constant speed of 15m/s for 5 seconds
- decelerated at a rate of 3.75m/s² for 4 seconds.

> The distance travelled (displacement) is given by the area under a velocity–time graph and the time axis.

$= \text{Area of OAX} + \text{Area of ABYX} + \text{Area of BCY}$

$= (\dfrac{1}{2} \times 3 \times 15) + (5 \times 15) + (\dfrac{1}{2} \times 4 \times 15) = \mathbf{127.5m}$

Graphs can also be drawn to represent **non-uniform** motion.

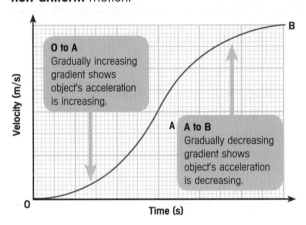

O to A
Gradually increasing gradient shows object's acceleration is increasing.

A to B
Gradually decreasing gradient shows object's acceleration is decreasing.

P2 Scalar and Vector Quantities

Scalar quantities have a **size** only, for example:

- mass
- energy
- speed
- time
- distance.

Vector quantities have **size** and **direction**, for example:

- velocity
- force
- acceleration
- displacement.

Quick Test

1. State the equation used to calculate acceleration.
2. An object travelling forwards has a acceleration of −5m/s. What does this tell you about the motion?
3. P2 Give an example of a scalar quantity and an example of a vector quantity.

Forces

P2 What is a Force?

A **force** occurs when two objects **interact** with each other. Whenever one object exerts a force on another, it always experiences a force in return.

The forces in an **interaction pair** are:
- **equal** in size
- **opposite** in direction and they act on different objects.

This is known as **Newton's Third Law.**

Forces and Friction

Some **forces** only occur as a response to another force.

When an object is resting on a surface:
- the object is pulled down onto the surface by gravity
- the surface pushes up on the object with an equal force.

This is called the **reaction of the surface**.

When two objects try to slide past one another, both objects experience a force that tries to **stop them moving**. This is called **friction**.

Objects don't have to be moving to experience friction. For example, the friction from a car's brakes stops it rolling down a hill.

Friction and the reaction of a surface arise in response to the action of an applied force, and their size matches the applied force up to a limit.

P2 Arrows are used when drawing diagrams of **forces**:
- The size of the arrow represents the size of the force.
- The direction of the arrow shows the direction the force is acting in, e.g. frictional forces always oppose motion.

N.B. Force arrows are always drawn with the tail of the arrow touching the object even if the force is pushing the object.

If more than one force acts on an object they will:
- add up if they are acting in the same direction
- subtract if they are acting in opposite directions.

The overall effect of adding or subtracting these forces is called the **resultant force**.

Force • Friction • Resultant force

Forces in Action

Forces, measured in **newtons (N)**, are **pushes** or **pulls**. They may be **different in size** and **act in different directions**. There are several types of force: gravity, magnetic forces and electrostatic forces are just some examples.

Forces can cause objects to **accelerate** or decelerate. They can also change the direction of an object, or the shape of an object.

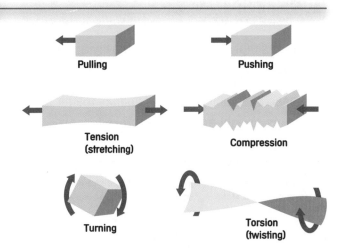

Pulling　　　Pushing

Tension (stretching)　　　Compression

Turning　　　Torsion (twisting)

Force, Mass and Acceleration

If an unbalanced force acts, the acceleration of the object will depend on:
- the resultant force applied to the object
- the **mass** of the object.

For example:

A boy pushes a trolley. He exerts an unbalanced force which causes the trolley to move and accelerate.

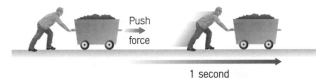

Push force

1 second

If two boys push the same trolley, it moves with a greater acceleration. (**More force = greater acceleration.**)

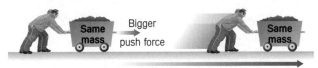

Same mass　Bigger push force　Same mass

1 second

If the first boy now pushes a trolley of bigger mass, it moves with a smaller acceleration than the first trolley. (**More mass = less acceleration.**)

Bigger mass　Push force　Bigger mass

1 second

If two trolleys with different masses move with a constant acceleration, the trolley with the larger mass will have to be pushed with more force than the trolley with the smaller mass. (**More mass = more force required.**)

Larger mass　Bigger push force　Smaller mass　Push force

The relationship between force, mass and acceleration is shown in this formula:

Resultant force (N) = Mass (kg) × Acceleration (m/s²)

A **newton (N)** can be defined as the force needed to give a **mass of one kilogram** an acceleration of one **metre per second per second** (1m/s²).

Example

A trolley of mass 400kg is accelerating at 0.5m/s². What force is needed to achieve this acceleration?

Force = Mass × Acceleration
= 400kg × 0.5m/s²
= **200N**

Forces

Weight and Mass

Weight is simply the force due to gravity acting on an object.

The **mass** of an object is the amount of matter that it contains. Weight and mass are linked by two related formulae:

> **Weight** (N) **= Mass** (kg) **× Gravitational field strength** (N/kg)
> **Weight** (N) **= Mass** (kg) **× Acceleration of free-fall** (m/s²)
>
>
>
> where: *g* = gravitational field strength or acceleration of free-fall

Without air resistance, a falling object near the Earth's surface would have an acceleration of 10m/s². This is known as the **acceleration of free-fall**, *g*.

The force which causes this acceleration is the weight of the object. The formula is **W = mg**.

> #### Example 1
>
> Calculate the weight of a stone of mass 0.1kg, if g = 10m/s².
>
> Weight = Mass × Acceleration of free-fall
>   = 0.1kg × 10m/s² = **1N**

Near the surface of the Earth the **gravitational field strength, g**, is 10N/kg, which means that every 1kg of matter experiences a downwards force, or has a weight, of 10N.

> #### Example 2
>
> Calculate the weight of a stone of mass 0.1kg on Earth, if g is 10N/kg.
>
> Weight = Mass × Gravitational field strength
>   = 0.1kg × 10N/kg = **1N**

N.B. Acceleration of free-fall and gravitational field strength are numerically the same, i.e. 10m/s² and 10N/kg. They also both have the same symbol, g.

Weight and Centre of Gravity

The **centre of gravity** (C of G) of an object is the point through which the **whole mass** of the **object** is considered to act. It can be thought of as the point where all the mass is concentrated.

For example, if you balance an object on the end of your finger, the centre of mass of the object is the point at which the object **balances**.

Objects with a wide base and a low centre of gravity, e.g. Bunsen burners, are more stable than those objects with a narrow base and a high centre of mass, e.g. ladders.

Quick Test

1. **P2** What is the resultant force on an object?
2. What is friction?
3. A trolley of mass 200kg is accelerating at 0.25m/s². What force is needed to produce this acceleration?
4. Calculate the weight of a stone of mass 0.2kg if g = 10m/s².
5. What is the centre of gravity of an object?
6. Explain why the object on the right is stable whereas the object on the left is unstable.

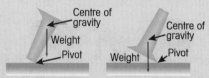

Terminal Velocity

When a skydiver jumps out of an aeroplane, the speed of his descent can be considered in two separate parts:

Before the parachute opens (when the skydiver is in free-fall)**:**

1. When the skydiver jumps, he initially accelerates due to the force of **gravity**.
2. As he falls, he experiences the **frictional force of air resistance** (R) in the opposite direction. At this point, **weight** (W) is **greater than R**, so he continues to accelerate.
3. As his velocity increases, so does the air resistance acting on him.
4. Air resistance increases until it's equal to W. The resultant force now acting on him is zero and his falling velocity becomes constant as forces are balanced. This velocity is called the **terminal velocity**.

After the parachute opens (when **air resistance** is greatly increased)**:**

5. When the parachute is opened, unbalanced forces act again because the upward force of R is greatly increased and is bigger than W.
6. The increase in R decreases his velocity. As his velocity decreases, so does R.
7. R decreases until it's equal to W. The forces acting are once again balanced and for the second time, he falls at a steady velocity, although slower than before. This is a **new terminal velocity**.

At **higher velocity**, falling objects experience **more drag**. If you **increase the area** of the object that's facing downwards, **you increase the drag**. The **terminal velocity** occurs when the drag is equal to the weight of the object.

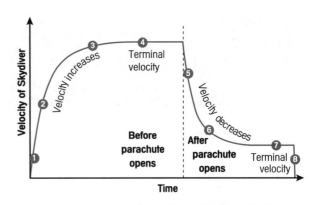

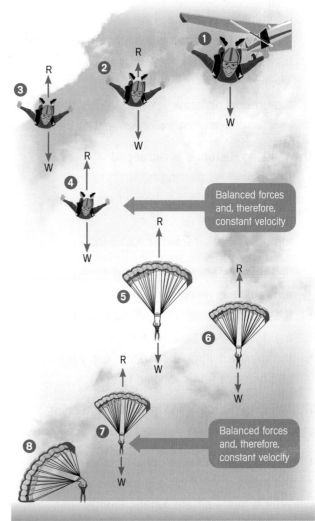

Experiments to Investigate Forces on Falling Objects

You can investigate terminal velocity using a tall tube filled with olive oil and a steel ball. Take measurements of distance fallen through the oil and time taken for each distance. The speed can be calculated. Measure the mass of the ball and, from the record of time and calculations of speed, calculate the acceleration. Use force = mass × acceleration ($F = ma$) to work out the force on the ball.

Forces

Stopping Distance

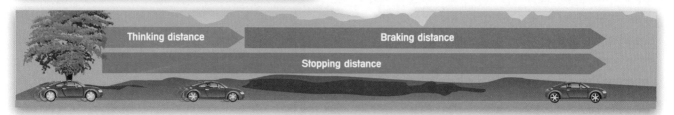

Thinking distance

Braking distance

Stopping distance

> Stopping distance = Thinking distance + Braking distance

The stopping distance of a vehicle depends on:

- the **thinking distance** – the distance travelled by the vehicle from the point the driver realises the need to brake to when the brakes are applied
- the **braking distance** – the distance it takes the vehicle to stop once the driver applies the brakes.

The **thinking distance** is **increased** if:

- the vehicle is travelling faster
- the driver is ill, tired or under the influence of alcohol or drugs
- the driver is distracted or isn't concentrating.

The **braking distance** is **increased** if:

- the vehicle is travelling faster
- there is poor weather / bad road conditions, e.g. if it's wet, slippery or icy
- the vehicle is in poor condition, e.g. worn brakes and tyres, or under-inflated tyres.

The thinking distance and braking distance of a vehicle depend on the vehicle's **speed**.

The braking distance of a vehicle is increased if:

- the **mass** of the vehicle is **increased** – a loaded vehicle has a greater **kinetic energy**
- the **friction** between the tyres and the road is **decreased** – a wet or greasy road surface reduces the amount of friction between the tyres and the road

- the **braking force** applied is **decreased** – a smaller force is exerted by the brake pads on the wheel discs if the pads are worn
- the vehicle is **travelling faster** – a faster vehicle has greater kinetic energy.

The thinking distance increases linearly:

- Double speed = Double the distance travelled whilst reacting (at constant speed)

The braking distance follows a squared relationship:

- Double speed = Quadruple the braking distance
- Triple speed = Multiply the braking distance by 9

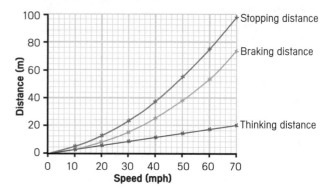

Quick Test

1. Draw a graph to show how the velocity of a falling object changes with time.
2. Explain the shape of the graph.
3. Explain how to investigate the forces acting on a falling object.
4. What does the stopping distance of a vehicle depend on?
5. What three factors can increase the thinking distance?

P2 Calculating Momentum

Momentum is a fundamental property of moving objects. It depends on:

- the **mass** of the object
- the **velocity** of the object.

Momentum can be calculated using the formula:

$$p(\text{kg m/s}) = m(\text{kg}) \times v(\text{m/s})$$

where: p is the momentum in kilograms metre per second (kg m/s), m is the mass in kilograms, v is the velocity in m/s

A moving car has momentum as it has both mass and velocity (speed in a certain direction). If the car moves with greater velocity then it has more momentum, providing its mass is the same.

For example, a car of mass 1200kg is moving with a velocity of 20m/s. Its momentum is 1200kg × 20m/s = 24 000kg m/s. If the car moves with a new velocity of 30m/s, then its new momentum is 1200kg × 30m/s = 36 000kg m/s.

P2 Conservation of Momentum

Momentum (like velocity) is a vector. It has…

- **size** (magnitude)
- **direction**.

The direction of movement is important when undertaking calculations involving momentum.

For example:

- Car A of mass 1400kg (moving from left to right) has a velocity of 20m/s to the right and, consequently, a momentum of 28 000kg m/s to the right.
- Car B of mass 1400kg (moving from right to left) has a velocity of 20m/s to the left, i.e. −20m/s, and momentum is −28 000kg m/s.

Positive velocity
Positive momentum

Negative velocity
Negative momentum

In a closed system, i.e. where no other external forces act, the total momentum before an event is equal to the total momentum **after the event**. This is called the conservation of momentum.

Example

Two cars are travelling in the same direction along a road. Car A collides with the back of car B and they stick together. Calculate their velocity after the collision.

Before

20m/s   9m/s

Car A mass 1200kg   Car B mass 1000kg

After

vm/s

Car A + Car B mass 2200kg

Momentum before collision:

= Momentum of A + Momentum of B

= (mass × velocity of A) + (mass × velocity of B)

= (1200kg × 20m/s) + (1000kg × 9m/s)

= 24 000kg m/s + 9000kg m/s

= 33 000kg m/s

Momentum after collision:

= Momentum of A and B

= (mass of A + mass of B) × (velocity of A + B)

= (1200 + 1000) × v = 2200v

Since momentum is conserved:

Total momentum before = Total momentum after

$$33\,000 = 2200v$$

$$\text{So, } v = \frac{33\,000}{2200} = \textbf{15m/s}$$

Momentum

P2 Momentum and Collisions

During a collision **momentum** is conserved.

When the car slows down during impact its momentum decreases. As it decreases, the passengers feel a force which can result in injury, e.g. whiplash.

The force experienced by a passenger during a collision depends upon the rate of changes of momentum. The quicker the change in momentum, the greater the force experienced.

Use the following equation to calculate the force:

$$\text{Force (N)} = \frac{\text{Change in momentum (kg m/s)}}{\text{Time taken (s)}}$$

Change in momentum = mv − mu
= m (v − u)

m = mass of object
u = initial velocity
v = final velocity

The quicker the body decelerates, the greater the force felt by the body.

Example 1

Calculate the force experienced when an 80kg man decelerates from 3m/s to rest (0m/s) in 0.5 seconds.

$$\text{Force} = \frac{80 \times (0 - 3)}{0.5} = \textbf{−480N}$$

Example 2

Recalculate the force experienced by the same man if he now increases the time taken to stop to 2 seconds.

$$\text{Force} = \frac{80 \times (0 - 3)}{2} = \textbf{−120N}$$

Compare the forces experienced in the collisions in Example 1 and Example 2.

P2 Reducing Stopping Forces

The stopping forces experienced in a collision can be **reduced** by:
* **increasing** the stopping or **collision time**
* **increasing** the stopping or **collision distance**.

All of the standard safety features reduce the stopping forces on the people in the car, e.g. air bags, seat belts and crush zones. This reduces the risk of injury.

P2 Newton's Third Law

Newton's third law states that forces come in pairs that are equal in size and opposite in direction, and act on different objects.

Air pushing helicopter up

Blades pushing air down

Quick Test

1. What is meant by the phrase 'conservation of momentum'?
2. How can the stopping forces experienced in a collision be reduced?
3. What is Newton's third law?

Moments

P2 Calculating the Size of Moments

Forces can be used to turn objects about a particular point – the **pivot point**. The turning effect of such a force is called the moment.

You can calculate the size of a moment by using the formula:

> **M = F × d**
> where: *M* is the moment of the force in newton-metres (Nm),
> *F* is the force in newtons (N), *d* is the perpendicular distance from the line of action of the force to the pivot in metres (m)

You can increase the size of the moment in two ways:
- **Increase** the value of the **force**
- **Increase** the perpendicular **distance**.

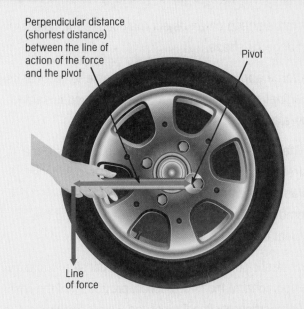

Perpendicular distance (shortest distance) between the line of action of the force and the pivot

Pivot

Line of force

P2 Law of Moments

When an object isn't turning, there must be a balance between:
- the **total moments** of the forces turning the object in a **clockwise direction**
- the **total moments** of the forces turning the object in an **anticlockwise direction**.

> Total clockwise moments = Total anticlockwise moments

This is called the law of moments.

A plank is pivoted at its centre of mass and has two forces, F_1 and F_2, pulling it downwards. The plank is balanced and not turning, so the total clockwise moment must equal the total anticlockwise moment.

> $F_1 \times d_1 = F_2 \times d_2$

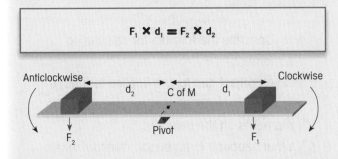

Example

A plank is pivoted at its centre of mass and has balanced forces acting. Calculate F_2.

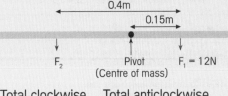

$$\text{Total clockwise moments} = \text{Total anticlockwise moments}$$

$$12N \times 0.15m = F_2 \times (0.4 - 0.15)m$$

$$\text{So, } F_2 = \frac{12N \times 0.15m}{0.25m} = \textbf{7.2N}$$

The upward forces on a light beam, which is supported at its ends, vary with the position of a heavy object placed on the beam.

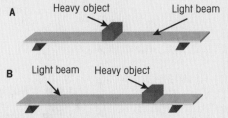

The upward forces on light beam A are different from those on light beam B.

Forces and Elasticity

Elastic Objects and Energy

A force acting on an object may cause the object to change its shape.

A force applied to an object that's able to recover its original shape when the force is removed is said to be **elastic**, e.g. a spring.

When a force is applied to a spring, work is done in stretching the spring. The energy stored is called **elastic potential energy**. When the force is removed, the energy stored is used to bring the object back to its original shape.

For elastic objects, like springs, the extension is directly proportional to the force applied, provided that the limit of proportionality is not exceeded. This is known as Hooke's law. The equation for this is as follows:

$$F = k \times e$$

where: F is the applied force in newtons
  e is the extension in metres
  k is the proportionality constant, called the spring constant, measured in units of N/m.

The graph shows the force-extension graph for an object that obeys Hooke's law.

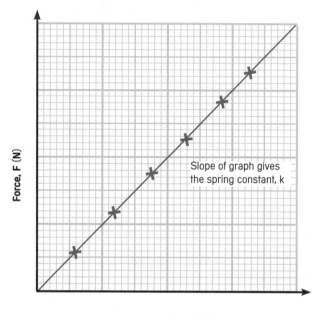

Slope of graph gives the spring constant, k

Force, F (N)

Extension, e (m)

Investigating Hooke's Law

Apparatus to Investigate Hooke's Law

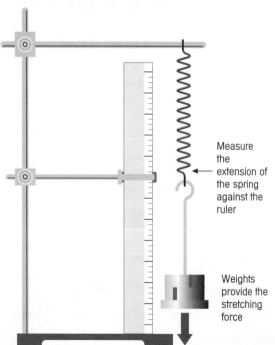

Measure the extension of the spring against the ruler

Weights provide the stretching force

You can investigate Hooke's law using the apparatus shown in the diagram.

You start by measuring the length of the spring without any mass added. You then add masses and record the mass, force, length of spring and therefore extension.

Quick Test

1. **P2** Describe the formula for calculating a moment.
2. **P2** An object has forces applied to it but it is not turning. What can you say about the moments on the object?
3. What happens to an elastic material when a force is applied and then removed?
4. State Hooke's law.

Elastic • Elastic potential energy

The Solar System

The Solar System was formed about 5000 million years ago:

1 The **Solar System** started as **dust** and **gas clouds**, pulled together by **gravity**.

2 This created intense heat. **Nuclear fusion** began and the Sun (a star) was born.

3 The remaining dust and gas formed smaller masses, which were **attracted** to the Sun.

The Sun is massive when compared with the planets and contains over 99 percent of the mass of the solar system.

Smaller masses in our solar system are:

- **planets** – eight large masses that orbit the Sun
- **moons** – small masses that orbit planets
- **asteroids** – small, rocky masses that orbit the Sun
- **comets** – small, icy masses that orbit the Sun
- **dwarf planets** – small masses (e.g. Pluto) orbiting the Sun.

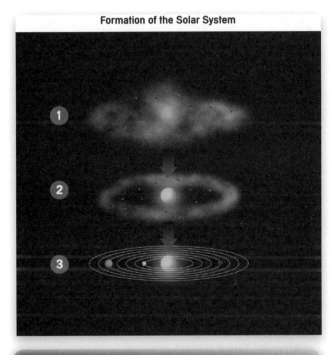

Formation of the Solar System

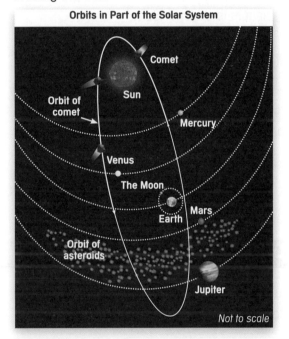

Orbits in Part of the Solar System

Comet

Sun

Orbit of comet

Mercury

Venus

The Moon

Mars

Earth

Orbit of asteroids

Jupiter

Not to scale

The Universe

The Universe is much older than the Sun and is approximately 14 000 million years old.

Not to scale

The Universe – contains billions of galaxies, with vast distances between them.

Our Sun

Our star – the Sun, 110 times wider than Earth

Our planet – the Earth, 12 800km in diameter

Our galaxy – the Milky Way, 100 000 light-years across, containing at least 200 billion stars.

Our galaxy

Astronomy

Gravitational Field Strength

The weight of an object is a force that measures how strongly gravity is pulling on the object. **Gravitational field strength** (g) tells you what force would be acting on a 1kg mass placed at a given point.

The gravitational field strength on Earth is taken to be 10N/kg. Its value is different on other planets and on the moon. On the moon it is 1.6N/kg. On Jupiter it is 26N/kg and on Neptune it is 14N/kg, for example.

Orbits

The gravitational force exists at all points in the Universe. It causes:
- moons to orbit planets
- planets to orbit the Sun
- artificial satellites to orbit the Earth
- comets to orbit the Sun.

The eight **planets** in the solar system follow nearly **circular orbits** around the Sun. **Comets** follow a more **elliptical path** around the Sun than planets.

Moons orbit planets rather than the Sun.

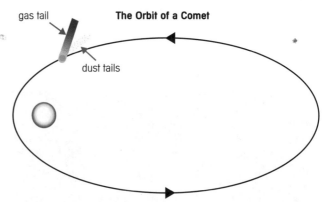

Comets orbiting close to the Sun show two very distinctive tails.

Orbital Speed

You can calculate the orbital speed of an object following a circular orbit using this formula:

$$\text{Orbital speed (m/s)} = \frac{2 \times \pi \times \text{Orbital radius (metres)}}{\text{Time period (s)}}$$

$$v = \frac{2 \times \pi \times r}{T}$$

Example

The orbital radius of the Earth is approximately 1.5×10^{11}m. Its time period is 3.2×10^7s. What is its orbital speed?

$$v = \frac{2 \times \pi \times 1.5 \times 10^{11}}{3.2 \times 10^7}$$

$$= \mathbf{2.9 \times 10^4 \ m/s}$$

Quick Test

1. How old is the Universe?
2. What is a galaxy?
3. What galaxy is our Solar System part of?
4. An object weighs 65N on Earth. What does it weigh on Jupiter?
5. What is the difference between orbits of comets and orbits of planets?
6. What is the orbital speed, in km/h, of a object that orbits a body once every 24 hours with an orbit radius of 6700km? (Give your answer to the nearest km/h.)

1 **a)** The graph shows three different journeys. Match statements
A, B and C with the labels **1–3** on the graph. **[2]**

A The person is moving at the fastest speed.

B The person is moving at the slowest speed.

C The person is stationary.

b) What does the gradient of a distance–time graph
tell you? **[1]**

2 **a)** A car is measured travelling 40 metres in 5 seconds. How fast is the car travelling?
Put a ring around the correct answer. **[1]**

200m/s   8m   20m/s   8m/s   200m

b) A motorcycle accelerates from rest and reaches a velocity of 30m/s in 4 seconds. What is the
acceleration of the motorcycle? Put a ring around the correct answer. **[1]**

120m/s^2 7.5m/s   120m/s   34m/s   7.5m/s^2

3 Which of the following statements are correct? Put ticks (✓) in the boxes next to the **two**
correct statements. **[2]**

Velocity–time graphs are used in lorry tachographs to make sure drivers rest for the appropriate time.

Friction is a force that always opposes motion.

The instantaneous speed is the maximum speed reached during a journey.

The gradient of a distance–time graph is the acceleration.

4 A person starts to walk in a straight line along a flat pavement. Explain what forces are involved in
the process of walking. **[4]**

Exam Practice Questions

5 A car of mass 1500kg is travelling along a road at a velocity of 45m/s.

a) What is the momentum of the car? [2]

b) What is the acceleration if the velocity increases from 45m/s to 55m/s in 4 seconds? [2]

6 Which of the following statements are correct? Put ticks (✓) in the boxes next to the **two** correct statements. [2]

The change in momentum depends on the size of the force acting and the time it acts for.

For an object moving in a straight line, if the driving force is larger than friction, the object will slow down.

If the resultant force on a car is zero, its momentum is constant.

7 A 150kg dodgem car travelling at 3m/s collides with a rubber wall in the fairground and rebounds with a speed of 2m/s.

a) What is the change in momentum? [2]

b) If the collision lasted for 0.5 seconds, what force acted on the dodgem car? [2]

c) Why did the driver bend his knees during the impact? [3]

8 a) What two things do you need to know in order to calculate the acceleration of an object? **[2]**

....

....

b) Draw lines between the boxes to match each statement with its meaning on a velocity–time graph. **[2]**

| Straight line with a positive gradient |

| Constant velocity |

| Straight line with a negative gradient |

| Deceleration |

| Horizontal straight line |

| Acceleration |

9 Tom has just started taking driving lessons and is interested in thinking, braking and stopping distances.

He is looking at the graph below.

a) Which of the graph lines, A, B or C, represents the thinking distance? **[1]**

....

b) How long would the braking distance be if a vehicle was travelling at 45mph? **[1]**

....

c) Write about any two factors which increase the thinking distance of a driver. **[2]**

....

....

10 List three safety features of modern cars that protect the occupants in the event of a collision. **[3]**

....

....

....

11 A skydiver of mass 60kg jumps from an aeroplane and free-falls without opening their parachute.

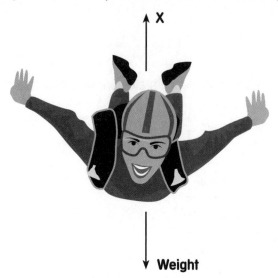

a) In the diagram of the free-falling skydiver, what is the name of the force X? **[1]**

b) Explain what happens to the force X as the skydiver accelerates. **[1]**

c) After 250m of free-fall, the skydiver no longer accelerates. What do we call this point? **[1]**

d) What value does the force X now have at (and beyond) this point when the skydiver is still in free-fall? **[1]**

12 What is the force on a car of mass 1100kg as it slows down from 50mph (22.3m/s) to 30mph (13.4m/s) in 20s? **[2]**

13 The diagram shows a crane lifting a container.

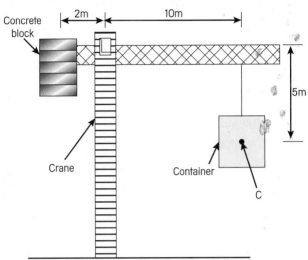

The container has a mass of 3000kg.

a) Calculate the weight of the container. **[1]**

b) The crane is balanced. What is a suitable value for the mass of the concrete block? **[4]**

14 a) What is the difference between the orbit of a comet and the orbit of a planet? **[2]**

b) Mars takes 687 days to orbit the Sun. Its average distance from the Sun is 228 million km.

Calculate the average orbital speed of Mars in m/s. **[3]**

c) What is the difference between the Universe and a galaxy? **[2]**

Mains Electricity

How Does Mains Electricity Work?

Mains electricity is very useful if it is used properly. When an appliance, such as a washing machine, is switched on, an electrical **circuit** between the **local substation and the appliance is completed**. This allows electrical energy to travel from the substation to the appliance through the **'live' and 'neutral' wires**.

Some appliances, for example those with metal cases, have an **earth wire**. This wire does not normally carry current but is there for safety. A three-pin plug is wired as shown.

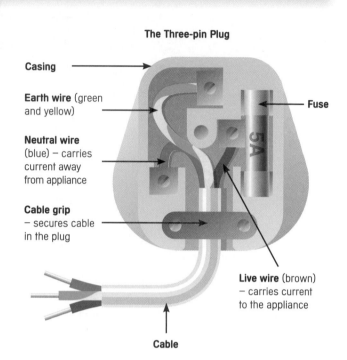

The Three-pin Plug

Casing

Earth wire (green and yellow)

Neutral wire (blue) – carries current away from appliance

Cable grip – secures cable in the plug

Fuse

Live wire (brown) – carries current to the appliance

Cable

Alternating Current and Direct Current

Mains electricity is supplied as **alternating current**.

A battery produces a steady current where the **voltage stays constant with time**. This is called **direct current**. The graph shows how the **voltage varies with time for alternating current** and for **direct current**.

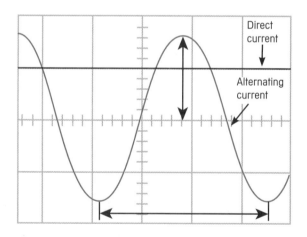

Direct current

Alternating current

Hazards of Mains Electricity

The table shows some hazards of electricity.

Hazard	Danger
Frayed cables	Wiring can become exposed
Long trailing cables	Might cause a trip or fall
Damaged plugs	Wiring can become exposed
Water around sockets	Water conducts, so can connect a person into a mains supply
Pushing metal objects into sockets	This connects the holder to the mains supply, which could be fatal

Key Words   **Mains electricity • Circuit • Alternating current • Direct current**

Electrical Safety

Circuit Breakers and Fuses

If an electrical fault occurs there is an increase in the current flow. A **fuse** or **circuit breaker** in the circuit provides a disconnection in the live wire, effectively switching off the circuit.

Depending on the type of electrical appliance, the plug will be fitted with fuses that have **different ratings**, e.g. 3A, 5A, 13A. When the current in the **fuse** wire exceeds the rating of the fuse it will **melt, breaking the circuit**.

The thicker the cable, the **higher** the rating of the **fuse value**. Fuses have to be replaced each time the circuit is overloaded.

Some modern circuits are protected by using circuit breakers, which **automatically** break an electric circuit if it becomes overloaded. Circuit breakers are easily **reset** by pressing a button.

Some circuits are protected by **Residual Current Circuit Breakers (RCCBs)**. These operate by detecting a **difference** in the current between the **live** and **neutral** wires. These devices operate much faster than a fuse.

Earthing

Devices that have outer **metal cases** are usually **earthed**. The outer case of an electrical appliance is connected to the earth pin in the plug through the earth wire.

The earth wire and fuse work together to protect the appliance (and the user).

This is what happens if a fault occurs:
1. The case will become live.
2. The current will then 'flow to earth' through the earth wire as this offers least resistance.
3. This overload of current will cause the fuse to melt (or circuit breaker to trip), breaking the circuit.

The appliance (and user) is therefore protected.

Some appliances, e.g. drills, are **double insulated**, and therefore have no earth wire connection.

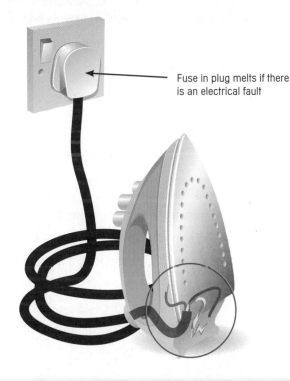

Fuse in plug melts if there is an electrical fault

Quick Test

1. Draw a graph to show voltage against time for a battery.
2. Why is pushing metal objects into a socket dangerous?
3. How does an RCCB operate?
4. What happens if a fault occurs in an appliance that is earthed?

Key Words   Fuse • Circuit breaker • Residual Current Circuit Breaker • Earthed • Double insulated

Energy and Potential Difference in Circuits

Energy Transfer

When an electrical **charge** (current) flows through a **resistor** (e.g. electrical device or appliance), the resistor gets **hot**. Some of the electrical energy is used but a lot of energy is wasted, which usually heats the surroundings.

In a filament bulb only 5% of the energy goes into light; the remaining 95% is wasted as heat energy. Less energy is wasted in power-saving lamps such as **Compact Fluorescent Lamps** (CFLs).

Power

The rate at which energy is transferred by an appliance is called the **power**.

Power can be calculated using the following formula:

$$P = I \times V$$

where: *P* is the power in watts (W), *I* is the current in amperes (amps, A) and *V* is the potential difference in volts (V)

For example, a vacuum cleaner rated at 1100W and using mains electricity (230V) provides a current of:

$$\frac{P}{V} = \frac{1100W}{230V} = 4.8A$$

A fuse with a rating of 5A would be suitable for the safe operation of this appliance.

Important factors to consider when buying household appliances (e.g. fridges, washing machines and dishwashers) are their energy efficiency and their power rating. Equally important is their ease of maintenance and location, which helps reduce heat loss and maintain efficiency.

Power can also be calculated using the following formula:

$$P = \frac{E}{t}$$

where: *P* is the power in watts (W), *E* is the energy transferred in joules (J) and *t* is the time in seconds (s)

The above relationship can also be written as $E = I \times V \times t$ since $P = I \times V$.

Circuits

A **circuit** is a complete loop that allows an **electrical current** to flow. **Electrons** flow around the circuit from the **negative electrode** of the power source to the **positive electrode**. But this was only discovered recently, so circuit diagrams are drawn showing the current flowing from **the positive to the negative electrode**.

Power • Current • Electrons

Energy and Potential Difference in Circuits

Series Circuits

For components connected **in series**:

- the total resistance (R) is the sum of the resistance of each component, $R = R_1 + R_2$
- there is the same current through each component, $I = I_1 = I_2$
- the total potential difference of the supply (V) from the battery is shared between the components, $V = V_1 + V_2$

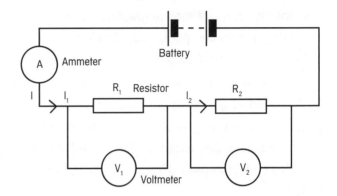

Parallel Circuits

For components connected **in parallel**:

- the potential difference across each component is the same, $V = V_1 = V_2$
- the total current through the whole circuit is the sum of the currents through the separate components, $I = I_1 + I_2$

A parallel circuit is appropriate for domestic lighting because each branch can be operated independently of the others. So a lamp (light) in one branch can be switched off without affecting the other branches.

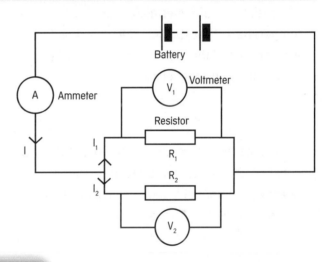

Investigating how Current Varies with Voltage

The current varies with voltage in wires, resistors, metal filament lamps and diodes. This can be investigated by using the circuit shown. (This circuit contains a resistor but this could be replaced by another component (resistor).)

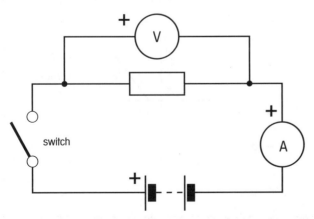

Quick Test

1. A washing machine has a power rating of 2300W and uses mains electricity at 240V. What fuse should be in the plug?
2. What happens to the current through individual components in a parallel circuit?
3. Why is a parallel circuit appropriate for domestic lighting?

Energy and Potential Difference in Circuits

Current–potential difference graphs show how the current through a component varies with the potential difference across it.

The resistance of a **light-dependent resistor (LDR)** depends on the amount of light falling on it. Its **resistance decreases** as the amount of **light** falling on it **increases**. This allows more current to flow.	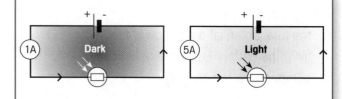
The resistance of a **thermistor** depends on its **temperature**. Its **resistance decreases** as the **temperature** of the thermistor **increases**. This allows more current to flow.	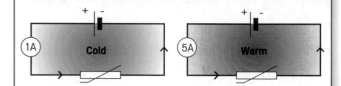
As long as the temperature of the **resistor** stays constant, the current through the resistor is directly proportional to the potential difference across the resistor. This is regardless of which direction the current is flowing, i.e. if one doubles, the other also doubles.	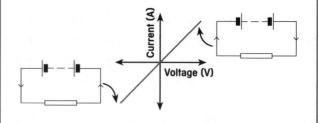
As the temperature of the **filament lamp** increases, and the bulb gets brighter, then the resistance of the lamp increases.	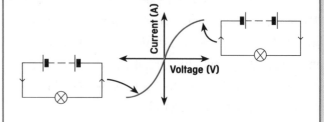
A **diode** allows a current to flow through it in **one direction only**. It has a very high resistance in the reverse direction so no current flows. A light-emitting diode (LED) emits light when a current flows through it in the forward direction. There is an increasing use of LEDs for lighting as they use a much smaller current than other forms of lighting and are cost-effective.	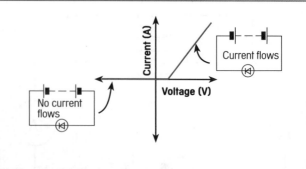

Energy and Potential Difference in Circuits

Current and Potential Difference

An electric **current** through a circuit is a **flow of negative charge**. The **size** of the electric current is the **rate of flow** of electric charge and is given by the following equation:

$$I = \frac{Q}{t}$$

where: I is the current in amperes (amps, A), Q is the charge in coulombs (C) and t is the time in seconds (s).

An electric current will flow through an electrical component (or device) if there is a **potential difference (voltage)** across the ends of the component.

(P2) The potential difference between two points in an electric circuit is the work done (energy transferred) per coulomb of charge that passes between the points.

Potential difference is given by the equation:

$$V = \frac{W}{Q}$$

where: V is the potential difference in volts (V), W is the work done in joules (J) and Q is the charge in coulombs (C).

Resistance and Ohm's law

The amount of current that flows through a component depends on:
- the **potential difference** across the component
- the **resistance** of the component.

All components resist the flow of current through them. Resistance is a measure of how hard it is to get a current through a component at a particular potential difference. Resistance is measured in **ohms**, which have the symbol Ω.

The greater the resistance of the components:
- the **smaller** the **current** that flows for a particular potential difference

OR
- the **greater** the **potential difference** needed to maintain a particular current.

To calculate the current, potential difference or resistance, the following equation is used:

$$V = I \times R$$

where: V is the potential difference in volts (V), I is the current in amperes (amps, A) and R is the resistance in ohms (Ω).

Quick Test

1. What happens to the resistance of a thermistor when its temperature increases?
2. State the equation used to calculate resistance.
3. Calculate the resistance of the lamp in the circuit.

4. Calculate the reading on the ammeter in this circuit if the bulb has a resistance of 20 ohms.

5. A filament lamp transfers 690J of energy using mains electricity at 240V. What is the amount of charge that passes through the circuit?

Electric Charge

Electrical Conductors

Metals are electrical conductors. In a metal structure, the atoms exist as ions surrounded by an electron cloud. If a potential difference is applied to the metal, the electrons in this cloud are able to move, creating the flow of a current.

When electrons are moving through the metal structure, they bump into the metal ions and experience resistance to the electron flow or current. Different conductors have different resistances according to how easily their electrons flow. For instance, copper is a better electrical conductor than iron.

Metal atoms (some people describe them as positive ions because they donate electrons into the 'sea' of electrons)

'Sea' of electrons (holds the metal atoms together)

Electrical Conductors and Insulators

The table lists materials ranging from the best conductor to the best insulator.

Silver is about 10^{27} times better at conducting charges than the plastic Teflon®. So to replace a 1mm diameter wire of silver in an electric circuit, you would need a bar of Teflon® far larger in diameter than the Moon's orbit around the Earth!

Material	Metal?	Conductor or Insulator?
Silver	Yes	Conductor (best)
Copper	Yes	Conductor
Aluminium	Yes	Conductor
Iron	Yes	Conductor
Graphite	No	Conductor
Silicon	No	Semiconductor
Most plastics	No	Insulator
Oil	No	Insulator
Glass	No	Insulator
Teflon®	No	Insulator (best)

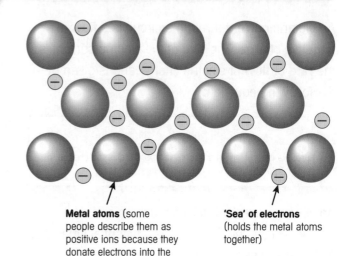

Conductor

Aluminium cable

Iron pan

Semiconductor

Silicon chip

Insulator

Glass

Teflon casing

P2 Static Electricity

Some insulating materials can become electrically charged when they are rubbed against each other.

Unless it is **discharged**, the electrical charge, called static electricity, stays on the material. Static electricity builds up when electrons (negative charge) are 'rubbed off' one material on to another. The material:

- **gaining** electrons becomes **negatively** charged
- **losing** electrons becomes **positively** charged.

For example, a Perspex rod rubbed with a cloth becomes positively charged and an ebonite rod rubbed with fur becomes negatively charged.

When two electrically charged objects are brought together they exert a force on each other.

They are either attracted or repelled:

- Materials with the **same** charge **repel** each other, e.g. Perspex and Perspex.
- Materials with **different** charges **attract** each other, e.g. Perspex and ebonite.

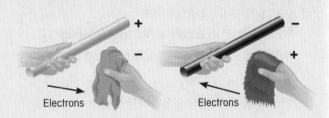

Perspex Rod Rubbed with Cloth   **Ebonite Rod Rubbed with Fur**

Electrons   Electrons

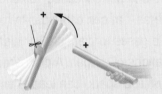

Perspex Rod repels a Perspex Rod

Perspex Rod attracts an Ebonite Rod

P2 Discharging Static Electricity

A **charged object** can be **discharged** (i.e. have the excess charge removed) by earthing it.

When an object discharges, electrons are transferred from the charged object to earth.

If you become charged and then earthed, you could get an **electrostatic shock**.

For example, you can become charged by friction between the soles of your feet and the floor if you're walking on an insulator such as carpet or vinyl. If you then touch a **water pipe**, e.g. a radiator, the charge is earthed and discharge occurs, giving you a shock.

Quick Test

1. Why are metals good electrical conductors?
2. Name a very good electrical insulator.
3. P2 Describe how you could charge up a Perspex rod.
4. P2 What will two materials with the same charge do if they are brought together?
5. P2 Is a material which gains electrons positively or negatively charged?

Electric Charge

Problems of Static Electricity

In some situations, static electricity can be a **nuisance**.

For example, static can cause:
- dirt and dust to be attracted to insulating materials, e.g. television screens and computer monitors
- some materials to cling to your skin.

In other situations, static electricity can be very **dangerous**:
- Flour mills and petrochemical factories have atmospheres that can contain extremely flammable gases (or vapours), or high concentrations of oxygen. A discharge of static electricity (i.e. a spark) can lead to an explosion. This is also true when aircraft are being refuelled.
- Static is dangerous in any situation where large amounts could flow through your body to earth, for example lightning.

Reducing the Danger of Static Electricity

The chance of receiving an electric shock can be **reduced** by:
- making sure appliances are correctly earthed
- using insulation mats effectively
- wearing shoes with insulating soles.

Lorries that contain inflammable gases, liquids or powders need to be earthed before unloading, as friction can cause a build-up of charge. This charge could lead to a spark, which could then ignite the flammable substances.

Anti-static sprays, liquids and cloths help to reduce the problems of static electricity by preventing the transfer of charge from one insulator to another. If there is no build-up of charge, there can't be any discharge.

P2 Using Static in Everyday Life

Static electricity is used in many ways, including spray painting, smoke precipitators and defibrillators.

Spray Painting

The paint particles are given a negative charge so that they repel each other, forming a fine spray. This ensures that the paint is applied evenly. The panel to be sprayed is positively charged, so it attracts the negatively charged paint. This means that less paint is wasted and even the back and sides of the object, in the shadow of the spray, receive a coat of paint. In a similar way, electrostatics can be used in crop spraying.

The paint gains electrons as it passes through the nozzle of the gun, so becomes negatively charged. The car panel has lost electrons, so is left positively charged. The car attracts the oppositely charged paint.

As the paint sticks to the car, the charges cancel so the car becomes neutrally charged and no more paint is attracted. The car receives an even coat of paint.

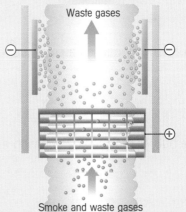

Spray Painting

Negatively charged nozzle

Negatively charged particles of paint

Car panel positively charged

Smoke Precipitators

Electrostatic dust precipitators can remove smoke particles from chimneys. Metal grids are installed in the chimney and are connected to a high potential difference (voltage). The dust becomes positively charged as it passes the grid, inducing a positive charge on the dust. The dust particles are attracted to the negatively charged plates, where they form large particles that fall back down the chimney when they are heavy enough, or if the plates are struck.

The dust particles become charged when they lose electrons.

Smoke Precipitator

Waste gases

Smoke and waste gases

Defibrillators

Electricity can be used to start the heart when it has stopped. Two paddles are charged and are put in good electrical contact with the patient's chest using gel.

Taking care not to shock the operator, charge is then passed through the patient to make the heart contract.

Quick Test

1. How can the danger of electrostatics be reduced?
2. Why is static electricity a danger where there are inflammable materials?
3. How is static electricity used in spray painting?

Exam Practice Questions

1 a) The build-up of charge is due to the transfer of positive electrons. Is this statement **true** or **false**? Explain your answer. **[1]**

....

....

b) Suggest two uses of electrostatics. **[2]**

....

....

2 a) Draw lines between the boxes to link each type of wire to its correct colour. **[2]**

Neutral		Green and yellow

Earth		Brown

Live		Blue

b) Double insulated appliances require neither a fuse nor an earth wire. Is this statement **true** or **false**? Explain your answer. **[1]**

....

....

3 a) A 12V supply causes a current of 0.3A to flow through a bulb. Calculate the resistance. **[2]**

....

....

b) The bulb is replaced by one with a resistance of 80Ω. What is the new current in the circuit? **[2]**

....

....

4 Toni has suspended a positively charged Perspex rod on an insulated plastic thread. What will happen if she brings a negatively charged ebonite rod close to the Perspex rod? **[1]**

....

....

5 Here is a table of data from an electrical experiment to find the resistance of three components.

Complete the table by filling in the missing values. **[3]**

Component	Voltage (V)	Current (A)	Resistance (Ω)
Lamp	8		4
Resistor		6	5
Coil	24	4	

6 Imran used the following circuit to carry out an experiment to find out what was in the mystery box. He measured the current and calculated the resistance for a range of temperatures. His results are shown in the table.

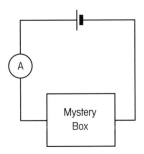

Temperature (°C)	100	80	60	40	20	0
Resistance (Ω)	50	62.5	83.3	125	250	260

a) i) What component might have been in the box? **[1]**

....

ii) What conclusion can be drawn from the table about the relationship between resistance and temperature for the component tested? **[1]**

....

b) The reading at 0°C doesn't fit the pattern. What mistake might Imran have made? **[1]**

....

7 **a)** Explain why an electric current causes an appliance to become hot. **[2]**

b) **i)** State the equation linking current, voltage and power. **[1]**

ii) An appliance has a power rating of 1100W and is designed to run from a 110V power supply. Calculate the current in the appliance when it is operating normally. **[2]**

c) Explain functioning of a fuse. **[3]**

d) What is the difference between alternating current (a.c.) and direct current (d.c.)? **[2]**

P2 8 **a)** Describe an experiment that you could carry out to find out whether two insulating rods had the same charge or opposite charges.

You should describe the equipment that you would use and how you would use it. **[4]**

b) Explain why it is not possible to charge a metal rod by rubbing it. **[2]**

9 An electrostatic paint spray is used to paint a car. The paint droplets are given a negative charge by the spray nozzle.

Spray Painting

Negatively charged nozzle

Negatively charged particles of paint

Car panel positively charged

a) The car is given an electric charge. Is this positive or negative? Explain your answer. **[2]**

b) Explain how charging the paint and the car improves the paint spraying process. **[4]**

Properties of Waves

Particle Motion in Waves

All waves **transfer energy** from one point to another **without** transferring any **particles of matter**. In the following diagrams, each coil of the slinky spring represents one particle.

There are two types of wave – **longitudinal** and **transverse**.

The slinky spring can be used to demonstrate both types of wave. A rope or water on waves and even sound can be used to demonstrate the nature of longitudinal waves whereas light travels as a transverse wave.

Longitudinal Waves	Transverse Waves
Each particle moves backwards and forwards about its normal position in the same plane as the direction of wave movement.	Each particle moves up and down about its normal position at 90° to the direction of the wave movement.
Direction of energy transfer — Hand moves in and out	Direction of energy transfer — Hand moves up and down

Key Features of Waves

The key features of waves are:

- **rarefaction** – area of low pressure
- **compression** – area of high pressure
- **wavelength** – the distance between corresponding points on two successive disturbances (λ)
- **frequency** – the number of waves produced (or that pass a particular point) in 1 second (f)
- **amplitude** – the maximum disturbance caused by a wave
- **period** – the inverse of frequency,
  $$T = \frac{1}{\text{frequency}} \quad \text{or} \quad T = \frac{1}{f}$$

N.B. Rarefaction and compression refer to longitudinal waves.

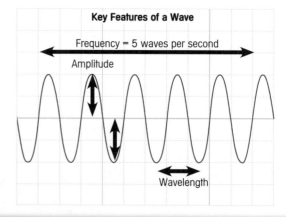

Longitudinal Wave

Direction of wave movement

Hand moves in and out — Rarefaction (coils further apart) — Compression (coils closer together)

Key Features of a Wave

Frequency = 5 waves per second

Amplitude

Wavelength

Key Words   **Wavelength • Frequency • Amplitude • Period**

The Wave Equation

Wave speed, frequency and wavelength are related by this formula:

> **Wave speed** = **Frequency** × **Wavelength**
> (metres per second, m/s)   (hertz, Hz)   (metres, m)
>
> where: v is the wave speed
> f is the frequency
> λ is the wavelength
>
> $$\frac{v}{f \times \lambda}$$

Example

A tuning fork of frequency 480Hz produces sound waves with a wavelength of 70cm when it is tapped. What is the speed of the wave?

Wave speed = Frequency × Wavelength

= 480Hz × 0.7m = **336m/s**

You can work out the frequency or wavelength by rearranging the wave speed formula.

Example

A radio station transmits on a frequency of 909 000Hz. If the speed of radio waves is 300 000 000m/s, on what wavelength does it transmit?

$$\text{Wavelength} = \frac{\text{Wave speed}}{\text{Frequency}}$$

$$= \frac{300\ 000\ 000\text{m/s}}{909\ 000\text{Hz}} = \textbf{330m}$$

What is the time period for these waves?

$$T = \frac{1}{f} = \frac{1}{909\,000} = \textbf{1.1} \times \textbf{10}^{-6}\textbf{s}$$

Wave Speed and Frequency

If a wave travels at a constant speed:

- **increasing** its frequency will **decrease** its wavelength
- **decreasing** its frequency will **increase** its wavelength.

Frequency is inversely proportional to wavelength.

If a wave has a constant frequency:

- **decreasing** its wave speed will **decrease** its wavelength
- **increasing** its wave speed will **increase** its wavelength.

N.B. *The speed of a wave is usually independent of its frequency and amplitude.*

Constant Speed

Frequency increased ⟵ ⟶ Frequency decreased

Constant Frequency

Wave speed decreased ⟵ ⟶ Wave speed increased

Calculating the Distance a Wave Travels

This formula is used to calculate the distance a wave travels at a given speed in a certain time:

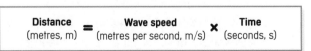

> **Distance** = **Wave speed** × **Time**
> (metres, m)   (metres per second, m/s)   (seconds, s)

Properties of Waves

P2 Diffraction

When waves move through a narrow gap or past an obstacle, they spread out from the edges. This is called diffraction. Diffraction is most obvious when:

- the size of the gap is similar to, or smaller than, the wavelength of the wave
- the waves that pass obstacles have long wavelengths.

Light waves (very small wavelengths) need a very small gap to be diffracted.

The fact that light and sound can be diffracted provides evidence of their wave nature.

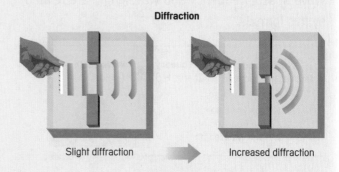

Diffraction

Slight diffraction → Increased diffraction

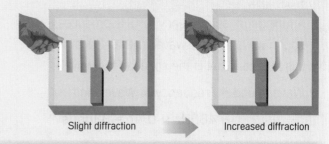

Diffraction

Slight diffraction → Increased diffraction

P2 Maximum Diffraction

Maximum diffraction occurs when the gap is the same width as the wavelength of the wave passing through it. This phenomenon limits the resolution and quality of the image produced by telescopes and optical microscopes. As light passes between two neighbouring particles, it is diffracted.

This diffraction results in the intensity and sharpness of the image being reduced. The light may also interfere with other diffracted light waves, distorting the image further.

Gap same size as wavelength – increased diffraction

Quick Test

1. Write a definition for frequency.
2. Write down the differences between a transverse and a longitudinal wave.
3. What do waves carry: matter, energy or both?
4. What is the amplitude of a wave?
5. What type of wave is a sound wave?
6. A water wave has a frequency of 5 hertz and a wavelength of 0.1m. What is the speed of the wave?
7. What is a student describing if they tell you the number of waves produced each second?
8. A station broadcasts signals at a frequency of 30MHz. If the speed of light is 3×10^8 m/s, what is the wavelength?
9. P2 When does maximum diffraction occur?

The Electromagnetic Spectrum

Electromagnetic Waves

The electromagnetic spectrum extends from high frequency or high energy (**short wavelength 10^{-15}m**) waves, e.g. gamma rays, to low frequency or low energy (**long wavelength 10^4m**) waves, e.g. **radio waves**.

Visible light is one type of electromagnetic radiation and is the only part of the electromagnetic spectrum that can be seen with the eye. It consists of seven primary bands of colour, from **red to violet**.

Electromagnetic waves are transverse waves and they all travel at the same speed in free space: 3×10^8m/s.

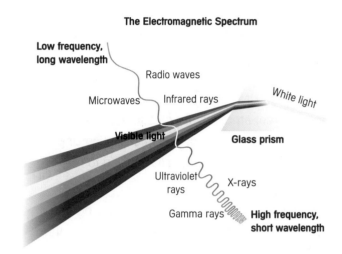

The Electromagnetic Spectrum

Low frequency, long wavelength

Radio waves

Microwaves

Infrared rays

White light

Visible light

Glass prism

Ultraviolet rays

X-rays

Gamma rays

High frequency, short wavelength

Uses of Electromagnetic Waves

Different parts of the electromagnetic spectrum can be used for different purposes.

Electromagnetic Waves	Uses
Radio waves	• Television and radio signals allow communication across the Earth
Microwaves	• Mobile phone networks and satellite communication (although there are potential risks of using mobile phones, e.g. possible links with brain tumours) • Cooking – water molecules absorb microwaves and heat up
Infrared	• Remote controls for televisions, etc. • Grills, toasters and radiant heaters (e.g. electric fires) • Optical fibre communication
Visible light	• Morse code with torches • Photography • Fibre optics
Ultraviolet	• Fluorescent lamps
X-rays	• Observing the internal structure of objects and materials • Medical applications
Gamma rays	• Sterilising food and medical equipment

Ionising Radiation

Ionising radiation can break molecules into bits called **ions**. **Ultraviolet** radiation, **X-rays** and **gamma rays** are examples of ionising radiation.

Ions are **very reactive** and can easily take part in other chemical reactions.

Electromagnetic radiations that are ionising have a high enough photon energy to remove an electron from an atom or molecule.

The Electromagnetic Spectrum

Cell Damage

Radiation **damages** living cells in different ways:

- The heating effect can damage the skin, e.g. sunburn.
- Ionising radiation can age the skin. It can also **mutate** DNA, which can lead to cancer.
- Different amounts of exposure can cause different effects, e.g. high intensity ionising radiation can destroy cells, leading to **radiation poisoning**.

Microwaves can heat materials by causing the water particles to vibrate. There may be a health **risk** from the low intensity microwaves of mobile phones and masts, but this is disputed. One study found no link from short-term use but other studies have found some correlation.

Ultraviolet waves can cause damage to surface cells, and blindness. Gamma rays can cause cancer and cell mutations.

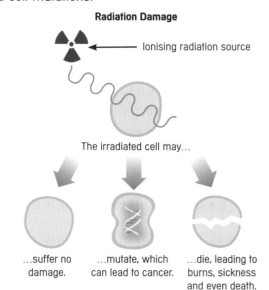

Radiation Damage

Ionising radiation source

The irradiated cell may…

…suffer no damage.

…mutate, which can lead to cancer.

…die, leading to burns, sickness and even death.

Radiation Protection

Microwave ovens have a metal case and a wire screen in the door to absorb microwaves and stop too much radiation escaping.

Other **physical barriers** are used to protect people:

- X-ray technicians use **lead screens**.
- Sunscreens and clothing can absorb ultraviolet radiation to help prevent skin cancer.
- Nuclear reactors are encased in thick lead and concrete.

Some radioactive materials emit ionising gamma radiation all the time. People going into areas of high radiation must wear a **radiation suit** as a shield and have a **radiation dose monitor**.

Quick Test

1. What is the speed at which all electromagnetic waves travel in a vacuum?
2. Give a use for the different parts of the electromagnetic spectrum.
3. Why can ions take part in other chemical reactions?
4. Give two ways in which radiation can damage cells.
5. How are people protected from microwaves from microwave ovens?

Key Words **Risk**

Reflection of Light

Light waves are transverse waves. They can be reflected, refracted and diffracted.

When light strikes a reflective surface it changes direction. This is called **reflection**.

The normal line is constructed perpendicular to the reflecting surface at the point of incidence. For reflected light the **angle of incidence (i)** is the same as the **angle of reflection (r)**. This is the law of reflection.

Light Reflected by a Plane Mirror

Object
Incident ray (travelling towards mirror)

Normal

Eye
Reflected ray (travelling away from mirror)

i   r

Plane mirror

Point of incidence

→ = Light ray   i = Angle of incidence   r = Angle of reflection

Refraction of Light

When light crosses an interface (a boundary between two transparent media of different densities) it changes direction. This is called **refraction**. No refraction occurs when the light enters the interface at 90°, i.e. along the normal.

The **refractive index** is a property of transparent media and can be determined using the equation:

> **Refractive index,** $n = \dfrac{\sin i}{\sin r}$
>
> where: *sin i* and *sin r* are the sine values of the **angles** of **incidence** and **refraction**.

The refractive index of air is 1.0, water is 1.33 and glass is 1.5.

Ray speeds up and is refracted away from the normal

Normal

Glass to air

Glass block

r

Air to glass

i

Normal

Ray slows down and is refracted towards the normal

Investigating Refraction of Light

The refraction of light can be investigated using the apparatus shown in the diagram. The block can be semicircular or you can use a triangular prism.

If you draw round the block and mark the position of the rays in air, then you can measure the angle of incidence and the angle of refraction as marked on the diagram.

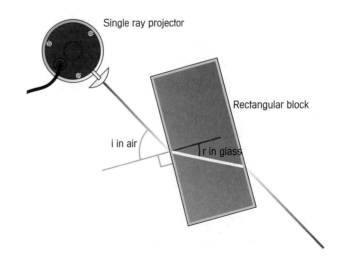

Single ray projector

Rectangular block

i in air

r in glass

Light and Sound

Investigating Refractive Index

You can use a similar set-up to that described on page 43 to investigate the refractive index of a material. You can change the angle of incidence and record it and its corresponding angle of refraction. From these results you can calculate the refractive index.

Total Internal Reflection

The **critical angle** is the maximum angle of incidence (measured from the normal) before **total internal reflection** (TIR) occurs. Different media have different critical angles.

Not all light is refracted when it leaves glass or water to travel through air. Some of the light is reflected from the surface:

1. If the angle of incidence is **less than** the critical angle, most of the light is refracted into the air.
2. If light hits the boundary at **exactly** the critical angle, it undergoes maximum refraction, emerging at 90° to the normal.
3. If the angle of incidence is **larger than** the critical angle, no light is refracted, i.e. all the light is **reflected** back into the medium. This is known as **total internal reflection**.

Different media (materials) have different critical angles.

Total internal reflection relies on light being refracted away from the normal as the light ray speeds up. Therefore, total internal reflection only occurs when:

- light travels from a medium with a high refractive index into a medium with a lower refractive index
- the angle of incidence is more than the critical angle.

The higher a medium's refractive index, the lower its critical angle. The critical angle, **c**, can be calculated using the following equation:

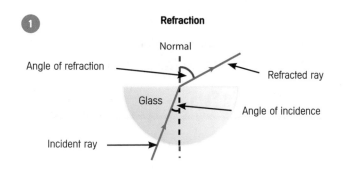

1

Refraction

Normal

Angle of refraction

Refracted ray

Glass

Angle of incidence

Incident ray

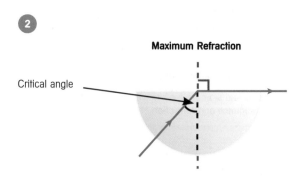

2

Maximum Refraction

Critical angle

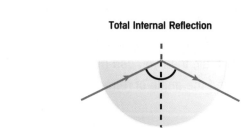

3

Total Internal Reflection

$$sin\ c = \frac{1}{n}$$

where: n = refractive index of the medium

Uses of Total Internal Reflection

Total internal reflection can be used in everyday life, including in optical fibres and bike reflectors.

Optical Fibres

Light that is incident on the glass–air boundary at an angle greater than the critical angle is reflected (TIR). In this way, light travels down the length of the fibre optic cable.

Fibre optics are used:

- to send digital signals for communication
- in endoscopes to observe tissues inside the body.

Bike Reflectors

In a bike reflector, the light undergoes total internal reflection at the plastic–air boundary and leaves the reflector parallel to the ray of light entering.

Reflectors

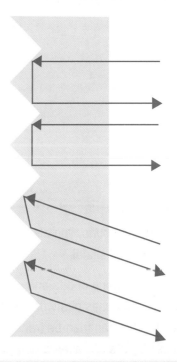

Quick Test

1. What is the relationship between refractive index, angle of incidence and angle of refraction?
2. Draw a diagram to show reflection of light in a plane mirror.
3. What is the critical angle?
4. What conditions must be satisfied for total internal reflection to occur?
5. What is the relationship between the critical angle and refractive index?

Light and Sound

P2 Analogue Signals

In amplitude modulation or frequency modulation (AM or FM), the amplitude or frequency of the carrier wave is changed by the input signal.

With frequency modulation the input signal causes the frequency of the carrier wave to change.

With amplitude modulation the input signal causes the amplitude of the carrier wave to change.

In both of these cases, the signal is called an analogue signal because it varies in exactly the same way as the information it's carrying. Analogue signals can have almost any value and can vary with time.

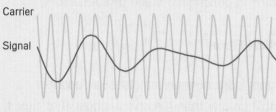

Frequency Modulation

Carrier

Signal

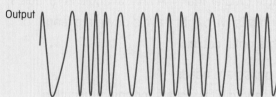

Output

Amplitude Modulation

Carrier

Signal

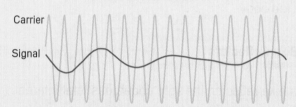

Output

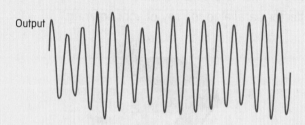

P2 Digital Signals

Information, including sound, can also be transmitted as a digital signal.

A digital signal is made up of bits and is converted into a digital code that uses bits with just two values (0 and 1). This can then be transmitted as a series of short bursts of waves called **pulses** (0 = no pulse, i.e. off; 1 = pulse, i.e. on). Pulses are produced by switching the electromagnetic carrier wave on and off.

When the digital signal is received, the pulses are decoded to produce a copy of the original sound wave or image.

Flat-screen TV used to Display Pictures Carried by Digital Signals

Key Words   Analogue • Digital

P2 Benefits of Digital Signals

Both digital and analogue signals:

- become weaker (their amplitude becomes smaller) as they travel, so they may have to be **amplified** at selected intervals
- can pick up random variations, called noise, which reduce the quality of the sound.

When a signal is amplified, any noise which has been picked up is also amplified.

Digital signals can travel long distances at a **higher quality** than analogue signals. This is because:

- **analogue signals** can have many different values, so it's hard to distinguish between noise and the original signal; this means that noise can't be completely removed
- **digital signals** only have two states, on (1) or off (0), so they can still be recognised despite any noise that's picked up; this means that any **interference** can be removed.

When digital signals carry noise, it's clear which parts of the signal represent 1 and 0, so the signal can be regenerated without the noise.

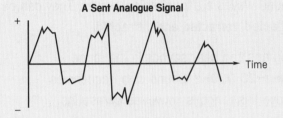

A Sent Analogue Signal

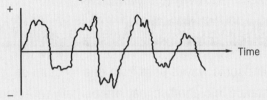

A Received Analogue Signal
Poor signal quality due to interference

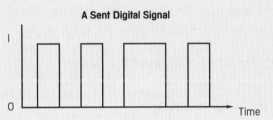

A Sent Digital Signal

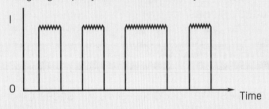

A Received Digital Signal
High signal quality as interference is easily removed

P2 Using Digital Information

The advantage of transmitting information using digital signals is that:

- information can be stored, e.g. on a hard drive, CD, DVD or **memory stick**
- information can be processed by computer, e.g. for spell checking, photo editing or music editing
- digital signals can carry more information.

Quick Test

1. What is an analogue signal?
2. How is a digital signal different from an analogue one?
3. Describe the benefits of digital signals compared to analogue signals.
4. Why doesn't noise affect digital signals?

Light and Sound

The Nature of Sound Waves

Sound waves are **longitudinal** waves. They can be **reflected, refracted and diffracted**.

Humans can **hear** sounds in the range **20Hz–20 000Hz**. Sound with frequencies above this range is known as ultrasound.

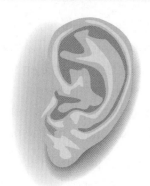

Using Ultrasound in Medicine

As ultrasonic waves pass from one medium or substance into another, they are partially reflected at the boundary. The time taken for these reflections is a measure of how far away the boundary is.

Ultrasound has many uses. Its uses in medicine include:

* pre-natal scanning
* imaging of damaged ligaments and muscles
* imaging of kidneys and destruction of kidney stones.

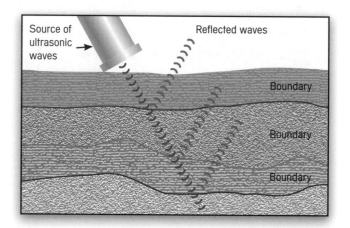

Source of ultrasonic waves

Reflected waves

Boundary

Boundary

Boundary

Measuring the Speed of Sound in Air

The simplest method to measure the speed of sound in air uses two microphones and a fast recording device such as a digital storage scope:

1. A sound source and the two microphones are placed in a straight line, with the sound source at one end.
2. The distance between the microphones (x), called microphone basis, is measured.
3. The time of arrival between the signals (delay) reaching the different microphones (t) is measured.
4. The speed of sound $= \dfrac{x}{t}$

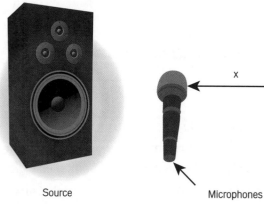

Source

x

Microphones

P2 Using an Oscilloscope

Sound waves can be displayed on an oscilloscope by using a microphone and loudspeaker as shown in the diagram.

You can use the arrangement shown to find the frequency of a sound wave. The voltage–time graph shown on the oscilloscope gives the time taken for one cycle of the wave (which is the period). Since T = $\frac{1}{f}$ you can work out the frequency.

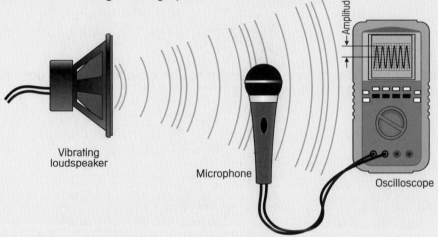

Vibrating
loudspeaker

Microphone

Oscilloscope

P2 Pitch, Frequency, Amplitude and Loudness

Pitch is related to frequency. High pitched sounds have high frequency and low pitched sounds have low frequencies. The amplitude of a sound wave is related to how loud the sound is. Loud sounds have high amplitude waves and quiet sounds have low amplitude waves.

Loud sound of low frequency	Loud sound of high frequency	Quiet sound of low frequency	Quiet sound of high frequency
A	B	C	D

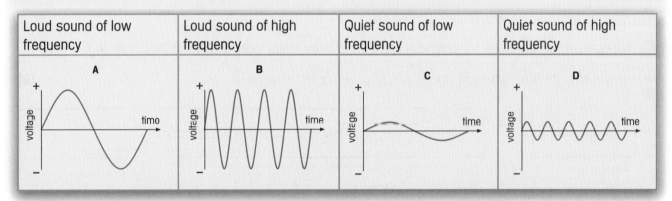

Quick Test

1. What is the frequency range for human hearing?
2. What technology makes use of the reflection of sound waves?
3. Sound waves can be diffracted through doors. What does this say about the approximate wavelengths of sound waves?
4. Describe how to measure the speed of sound.

Exam Practice Questions

1 A student shines a ray of light through a glass block, as in the diagram shown.

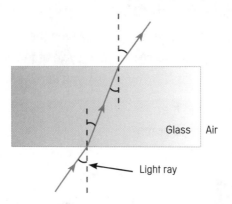

Glass   Air

Light ray

a) What is happening to the light ray in the diagram as it enters and leaves the glass block?   **[1]**

b) Explain why this happens.   **[3]**

2 A 3m wave has a frequency of 12Hz. At what speed is it travelling?   **[1]**

3 Below are three terms used to describe waves and three statements explaining their meaning.

Draw a straight line from each term to join it to the correct statement.   **[2]**

Amplitude		A measurement of how much energy a wave carries

Frequency		The distance between the corresponding points on two adjacent cycles

Wavelength		The number of waves made per second by a source

4 What is the wavelength of the waves used by a mobile phone, which have a frequency of 900MHz? (The speed of electromagnetic waves in a vacuum is 3×10^8 m/s.) **[2]**

5 Different parts of the electromagnetic spectrum are used for communication. For example, visible light is used for photography and Morse code with torches.

a) From the list below, link the type of radiation (**A**, **B** and **C**) with the mode of communication (**1**, **2** and **3**).

A Microwaves	**1** Optical fibre communication
B Radio waves	**2** Mobile phones
C Infrared	**3** TV

[3]

b) The electromagnetic spectrum is shown below, with wavelengths shown in metres. On the spectrum label the positions of microwaves, radio waves and infrared using the letters **A**, **B** and **C** (as above). **[3]**

Visible light

10^3 10^{-2} 10^{-5} 10^{-6} 10^{-8} 10^{-10} 10^{-12}

c) Sound waves are also used in communication. Calculate the wavelength of a sound wave if the speed of sound in air is 330m/s and the frequency is 2000Hz. **[2]**

d) Sound waves travel a lot faster in water than in the air; in fact approximately 1400m/s. Explain why sound waves travel faster in water. **[3]**

Exam Practice Questions

6 A ray of light travels from Perspex to the air.

a) Explain why the ray bends as it moves from Perspex to the air. **[2]**

b) There is an angle of incidence at which the refracted ray is at 90° to the normal. What is this angle called? **[1]**

c) Explain how an endoscope works. **[6]**

P2 **7** What is the difference between an analogue signal and a digital signal? **[2]**

8 **a)** List these electromagnetic waves in order of increasing wavelength.

Infrared   Radio waves   Ultraviolet   Visible light **[2]**

P2 **b)** The people who live in a village surrounded by hills cannot receive mobile phone signals. However they can receive long wave radio broadcasts. Use ideas about diffraction to explain why this is the case. **[3]**

9 **a)** Describe how to find the speed of sound in air. Include the equipment needed, what measurements should be made, and how the measurements will be used to find the speed of sound. **[6]**

....

....

....

....

....

....

....

P2 **b)** Describe how this equipment and the graph shown can be used to find the frequency of a sound wave.

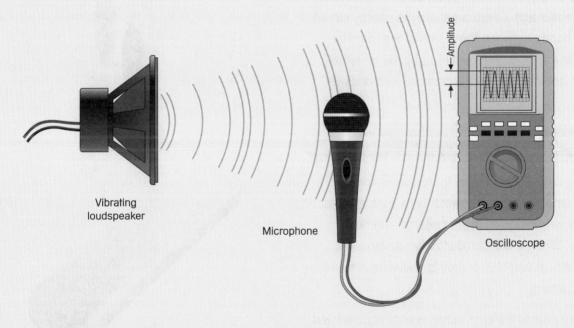

Vibrating loudspeaker

Microphone

Oscilloscope

[3]

....

....

....

....

Energy Transfer

Forms of Energy

Energy comes in different forms. Examples are potential and **kinetic energy**, chemical energy, nuclear energy, thermal energy, light energy and sound energy.

Potential energy is energy that is stored. Two examples of this type of energy are: **gravitational potential energy**, which is energy stored by an object being raised up in a gravitational field, e.g. a ball on top of a hill; and elastic strain energy, which is energy stored in things that are stretched, e.g. springs.

A cuckoo clock stores energy in two weights: one to run the mechanism that turns the hands, and one to make the cuckoo sing on each hour.

Kinetic energy is the energy an object has because of its movement. Chemical energy is energy stored in the bonds between the atoms of the material. Nuclear energy is energy stored by the extremely strong bonds between the particles in a nucleus.

Energy Transfers

Energy can be transferred from one form to another. For example, when you switch on a light, electrical energy is transferred to light energy and heat energy. When a ball is rolled down a slope, its gravitational potential energy is transferred to kinetic energy.

In every energy transfer, some energy is converted to internal energy, which shows itself as heat.

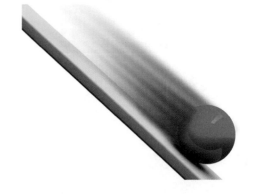

Conservation of Energy

The **law of conservation of energy** states that **energy cannot be created or destroyed**, simply transferred from one form to another.

When considering energy transfers, you need to remember that some of the energy in the process will be converted to internal energy (heat). Some energy transfers are more efficient than others.

Key Words Energy • Kinetic energy • Gravitational potential energy • Law of conservation of energy

Sankey Diagrams

Many devices take in energy in one form and transfer the energy into another form. In doing so, only part of the energy is usefully transferred to where it's wanted and in the form that's wanted.

The remaining energy is transferred in a **non-useful way**, i.e. is **wasted**. Wasted energy becomes increasingly spread out and so **warms its surroundings**. In this form it is difficult to use for further energy transfers.

For example, a light bulb transforms electrical energy into light energy. But most of the energy is wasted and the bulb becomes very hot.

A diagram that shows the relative proportions of energy transfers using arrows is called a **Sankey diagram**. The **widths of arrows** are proportional to the **amount of energy** they represent.

Sankey Diagram of a Light Bulb

Light energy
10J

Electrical energy
100J

Heat energy
90J

Electrical appliances transfer energy for different uses and some of the energy is wasted:
- A kettle transfers energy in the form of heat (to the water), but energy is also wasted as heat (to the kettle and air) and as sound.
- An electric motor (e.g. drill, washing machine) transfers kinetic energy, but energy is also wasted in the form of heat and sound.

Energy Efficiency

The **efficiency** of a device refers to the proportion of energy (or power) that is usefully transferred. **The greater the proportion** of energy (power) that is usefully transferred, the more efficient and the more **cost-effective** the device is.

Efficiency values are usually expressed either as a **percentage** or as a **decimal** number.

Efficiency can be calculated using the following equation:

$$\text{Efficiency} = \frac{\text{Useful energy or useful power out}}{\text{Total energy or total power in}} \times 100\%$$

For example, only a quarter of the energy supplied to a television is usefully transferred into light and sound.

The rest is wasted, so it's only 0.25 or 25% efficient.

Quick Test

1. State the law of conservation of energy.
2. List three forms of energy.
3. When energy is transferred, part of it may be useful. What happens to the rest?
4. A small wind turbine requires 2000J of energy from the wind but only provides 250J of useful electrical energy. What is the efficiency of the turbine as a percentage?
5. What is a Sankey diagram?

Energy Transfer

Conduction

Conduction is the transfer of energy by heating without the substance itself moving.

For example, metals are good **conductors** of energy:

- As a metal becomes hotter the **atoms vibrate** more vigorously.
- This additional energy is transferred to the cooler parts of the metal by the **free electrons** that roam throughout the metal.

Insulators are materials that have few or no free electrons, so they can't readily transfer their energy by heating.

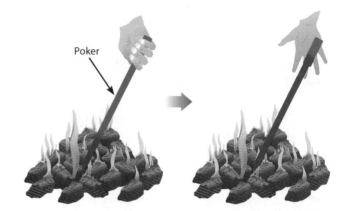

Poker

Heat energy is conducted up the poker as the hotter parts transfer energy to the colder parts

Convection

Convection is the transfer of energy by heating through the movement of particles.

Convection occurs in liquids and gases, creating **convection currents**:

① Particles in the liquid or gas nearest the energy source move **faster**, causing the substance to **expand** and become **less dense**.

② The warm liquid or gas now rises vertically. As it does so it **cools**, becomes **denser** and eventually sinks.

③ The colder, denser liquid or gas moves into the space created (close to the heat source) and the cycle repeats.

Liquid

Red dye crystals show the convection current in water under a heat source

← Candle

Gas
Circulation of air caused by a radiator

Air cools, becomes denser and sinks

Air warms up, becomes less dense and rises

Cooler air replaces air that has risen

Convection is used by 'radiators' to heat rooms.

Radiation

Hot objects **emit** mainly **infrared radiation**, an electromagnetic wave which can pass through a vacuum, i.e. no medium is needed for its transfer.

The amount of radiation given out or taken in by an object depends on its surface.

Dark, matt surfaces emit more radiation than light, shiny surfaces **at the same temperature**.

Dark, matt surfaces are better absorbers (poorer reflectors) of radiation than light, shiny surfaces **at the same temperature**.

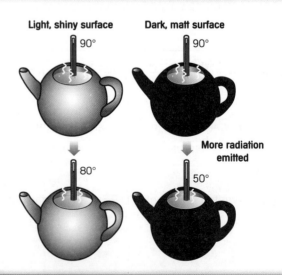

Light, shiny surface   Dark, matt surface

90°   90°

80°   More radiation emitted

                        50°

Conduction • Conductor • Insulator • Convection

Insulation

Clothing can be designed to reduce heat loss from the human body by conduction, convection and radiation. For example, several thin layers of fabric will reduce heat loss by trapping air between them.

Design features in the home help to **save energy** by reducing heat loss by **conduction**, **convection** and **radiation**. This table explains how.

Method of Insulation	Reduces:	How?
Fibreglass (or mineral wool) roof insulation	Conduction and convection	By trapping layers of air (a very good insulator) between the fibres
Reflective foil on walls	Radiation	By reflecting heat energy back into the room
Foam cavity wall insulation	Conduction and convection	By trapping air in the foam (the air is an insulator and prevents conduction; being trapped stops it moving and so prevents convection)
Double glazing	Conduction and convection	By trapping air between the panes of glass
Draught excluders	Conduction and convection	By keeping as much warm air inside as possible

Heat Loss in a House

Quick Test

1. Explain how heat is conducted through a metal.
2. Explain how convection occurs in liquids and gases.
3. Which type of surface would you use in a bar of an electric fire at a given temperature: a light, shiny surface or a dark, matt surface? Explain your answer.
4. Explain what types of energy transfer are reduced by using roof insulation and how it reduces this energy transfer.

Work and Power

Work

When lifting an object, the force applied will be the same as the weight of the object, measured in newtons:

> **Weight** (N) **=** **Mass** (kg) **✗** **Gravitational field** (N/kg)

Work is done whenever a **force** moves an object.

Energy is **transferred** to the object. You do work and develop power during everyday activities, for example:

- **lifting** weights
- **climbing** stairs
- **pulling** a rubbish bin
- **pushing** a shopping trolley.

Energy is needed to do work. Both energy and work are measured in **joules (J)**.

Work done is equal to the energy transferred (from one form to another).

> **Work done** (J) **=** **Energy transferred** (J)

The amount of work done depends on the:
- **size of the force** (in newtons)
- **distance** the object is moved (in metres).

> **Work done** **=** **Force applied** **✗** **Distance moved in direction**
> (J)   (N)   **of force** (m)

Power

Power is a measure of how quickly work is done, i.e. the rate of energy transfer. Power is measured in **watts (W)**.

Power, work done and time taken are linked by this formula:

$$\text{Power (W)} = \frac{\text{Work done (J)}}{\text{Time (s)}}$$

Example 1

A girl does 2400 joules of work when she runs up a flight of stairs in 8 seconds. Calculate her power.

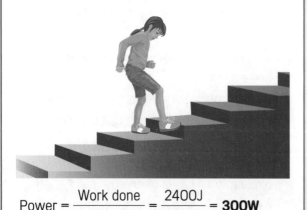

$$\text{Power} = \frac{\text{Work done}}{\text{Time}} = \frac{2400J}{8s} = \textbf{300W}$$

The **work done** and **power** formulae can be rearranged to work out distance moved or time taken.

Example 2

A crane does 200 000J of work when it lifts a load of 25 000N. The power of the crane is 50kW.

Calculate the time taken to move the load.

$$\text{Time} = \frac{\text{Work done}}{\text{Power}}$$

Power must be in watts

$$= \frac{200\ 000J}{50\ 000W} = \textbf{4s}$$

Gravitational Potential Energy

The **gravitational potential energy (GPE)** of an object is the energy stored due to:

- its position in the Earth's gravitational field (height)
- its **mass**.

Any object with the **potential** to fall has gravitational potential energy, for example a person standing on a diving board (before they jump off).

Man A standing on a higher diving board will have **more GPE** than man B standing on a lower diving board (providing they have the same mass). This is because the higher man is further away from the ground.

Man C (a heavier man), standing on the **same diving board** as man A will have **more GPE**. This is because the heavier man has a **bigger mass**.

You can calculate GPE using this formula:

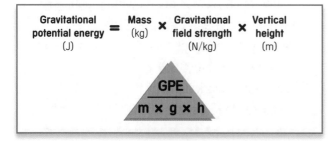

| Gravitational potential energy (J) | = | Mass (kg) | × | Gravitational field strength (N/kg) | × | Vertical height (m) |

$$\frac{GPE}{m \times g \times h}$$

Example 1

A skier of mass 80kg gets on a ski lift which takes her from a height of 1000m to a height of 3000m.

By how much does her gravitational potential energy increase?

= 80kg × 10N/kg × (3000m − 1000m)

= 80kg × 10N/kg × 2000m

= 1 600 000J (or 1600kJ)

N.B. Work done by the ski lift motor has been transferred into gravitational potential energy for the skier.

Example 2

A ball is kicked vertically upwards from the ground.

Its mass is 0.2kg and it increases its gravitational potential energy by 3J when it reaches the top point in its flight. What height does the ball reach?

Rearrange the formula:

$$\text{Vertical height} = \frac{GPE}{\text{Mass} \times \text{Gravitational field strength}}$$

$$= \frac{3J}{0.2kg \times 10N/kg} = \textbf{1.5m}$$

Work and Power

Kinetic Energy

Kinetic energy is the energy an object has because of its movement. A ball rolling along the ground, a car travelling along a road and a boy running all have kinetic energy.

The kinetic energy of an object depends on:
- its **mass** (kg)
- its **speed** (m/s).

You can calculate kinetic energy by using this formula:

$$\text{Kinetic energy (J)} = \frac{1}{2} \times \text{Mass (kg)} \times \text{Speed}^2 \text{ (m/s)}^2$$

$$\frac{KE}{\frac{1}{2} \times m \times v^2}$$

> **Example**
>
> A car of mass 1000kg is moving at a speed of 10m/s. How much kinetic energy does it have?
>
>
>
> $$\begin{aligned}\text{Kinetic energy} &= \frac{1}{2} \times \text{Mass} \times \text{Speed}^2 \\ &= \frac{1}{2} \times 1000\text{kg} \times (10\text{m/s})^2 \\ &= \textbf{50 000J (or 50kJ)}\end{aligned}$$

Gravitational Potential Energy and Kinetic Energy

When an object falls, it converts **gravitational potential energy (GPE)** into **kinetic energy (KE)**. For example, this happens when:
- a diver jumps off a diving board
- a ball rolls down a hill
- a skydiver jumps out of a plane.

As an object falls, the GPE is converted into kinetic energy.

Remember:

$$GPE = mgh, \quad KE = \frac{1}{2}mv^2$$

If all of the GPE is turned into KE:

$$mgh = \frac{1}{2}mv^2$$

The *m* on each side cancels, leaving:

$$gh = \frac{1}{2}v^2 \text{ or } gh = \frac{v^2}{2}$$

This can be rearranged to calculate the height, *h*:

$$h = \frac{v^2}{2g}$$

> **Example**
>
> A pot of paint falls from the top of some step ladders. Just before it hits the ground it has a velocity of 8m/s. From what height did it fall? (Remember g = 10 m/s².)
>
> $$h = \frac{(8)^2}{2 \times 10} = \frac{64}{20} = \textbf{3.2m}$$

> ## Quick Test
>
> 1. The amount of electrical energy transferred by a very bright light bulb is 200J/s. What is the power rating of the bulb?
> 2. A washing machine with a power consumption of 1600W is on for 45 minutes. How much work is done by the machine?
> 3. What happens to the size of the kinetic energy of an object if its speed is doubled?
> 4. What is the unit of GPE?
> 5. How does work done by the ski lift on the skier relate to increase in GPE of a skier?

Energy Resources and Electricity Generators

Electricity

Electricity is a **secondary** energy source. This means it's generated from another energy source, e.g. coal, nuclear power, etc.

Electricity is a very useful energy source as it can be easily transmitted over long distances and used in many ways.

Generating Electricity

The main primary energy sources that humans use are fossil fuels (oil, coal, gas), nuclear fuels, biofuel (e.g. wood), wind, waves and radiation from the Sun.

To generate electricity, fuel is burned to produce heat:

1. The heat is used to boil water, which produces **steam**.
2. The steam drives the **turbines**, which power the **generators**.
3. Electricity produced in the generators is sent to a step-up **transformer** and then to the **National Grid**.
4. To reduce energy losses, the National Grid distributes electricity to homes and businesses at high **voltages**.
5. The high voltages are stepped down by a transformer to the mains supply voltage in our homes (230V).

Power stations that burn fossil fuels like coal produce carbon dioxide, a greenhouse gas. This contributes to global warming and climate change.

Nuclear power stations release energy owing to changes in the **nucleus** of **radioactive** substances. They don't produce carbon dioxide but they do produce radioactive waste.

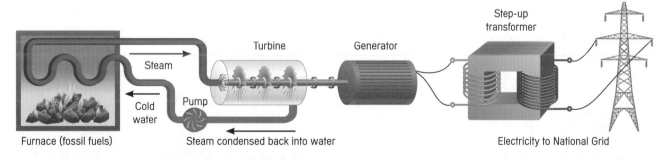

Furnace (fossil fuels) · Steam · Cold water · Pump · Steam condensed back into water · Turbine · Generator · Step-up transformer · Electricity to National Grid

Renewable Energy

Conventional energy supplies are running out, and both nuclear and fossil fuels cause environmental damage.

The burning of fossil fuels releases carbon dioxide into the atmosphere, contributing to global warming and climate change. This means that **alternative energy sources** are becoming more important.

Alternative ways to generate electricity include:
- wind
- waves
- hydroelectric power
- biofuel (e.g. wood)
- solar power
- geothermal power.

These **renewable** energy sources are **primary energy sources** and will not run out like fossil fuels.

Energy Resources and Electricity Generators

Non-renewable Energy Sources

We depend on **non-renewable energy sources** (e.g. coal, oil, gas and nuclear) for most of our energy needs. They can't be replaced within a lifetime, so they will eventually run out.

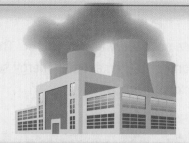

Source	Advantages	Disadvantages	Start-up Time
Nuclear	• Cost of fuel is low • Rate of fuel use is low • Doesn't produce CO_2 and SO_2 emissions into the atmosphere	• Radioactive waste produced • Difficulty of storing radioactive material for thousands of years • Building new power stations is very costly • Decommissioning is very costly • Risk of accidents and radioactive contamination	Longest
Coal	• Relatively cheap and easy to extract	• Burning coal produces CO_2 (**Greenhouse effect**) and SO_2 (**acid rain**) emissions into the atmosphere • Perhaps only several hundred years of coal left	
Oil	• Has been relatively easy to find • Perhaps large amounts of reserve stocks available	• Burning produces CO_2 and SO_2 emissions into the atmosphere • Significant risk of spillage and pollution • Destruction of wildlife habitats	
Gas	• Has been relatively easy to find • Perhaps large amounts of reserve stocks available • Doesn't produce as much SO_2 emissions into the atmosphere as coal or oil	• Burning produces CO_2 and SO_2 emissions into the atmosphere • Expensive pipelines and networks are required • Visual pollution of landscape • Destruction of wildlife habitats	Shortest

Quick Test

1. Name five primary energy sources used to generate electricity.
2. P2 Burning fossil fuels releases carbon dioxide into the atmosphere. What two problems does this contribute to?
3. P2 Give one advantage and one disadvantage of coal as an energy source.
4. P2 Give one advantage and one disadvantage of gas as an energy source.

Energy Resources and Electricity Generators

Renewable Energy Sources

Renewable energy sources will not run out because they are continually being replaced. Most renewable energy sources are caused by the Sun or moon.

The Sun causes:

- evaporation, which results in rain and flowing water
- convection currents, which result in winds that create waves.

The gravitational pull of the moon creates tides.

Renewable energy sources can be used directly to drive turbines and generators. New sources include **biofuels**, which can be solid, liquid or gas. Biofuels are obtained from lifeless or living biological material.

Biofuels include:

- liquid ethanol (derived from fermented plant material such as sugar cane)
- methane gas (from sludge digesters)
- straw, nutshells and woodchip.

Often small-scale productions can be set up and built locally to provide electricity, e.g. solar cells for homes and roadside signs.

P2 Source	Advantages	Disadvantages
Wind turbines	• No fuel and little maintenance • No polluting gases produced • Can be built offshore	• Land-based turbines give visual and noise pollution • High initial capital building costs • Not very flexible in meeting demand • Variation in wind affects output
Tidal and waves	• No fuel required • No polluting gases produced • Barrage water can be released when demand is high	• Visual pollution and hazard to shipping • Can destroy / alter wildlife habitats • Variations in tides / waves affects output • Very high capital costs to build
Hydroelectric	• Fast start-up time • No polluting gases produced • Water can be pumped back to the reservoir when demand is low	• Involves damming upland valleys • Destruction of wildlife habitats • Needs adequate rainfall • Very high initial costs
Solar cells	• Uses light from the Sun • Useful in remote locations • No polluting gases emitted • Small-scale production possible	• Depends on light intensity • Use of high cost semiconductor materials • Efficiency is poor • Visual pollution of large areas of solar panels
Biofuels	• Flexible product • Cost-effective	• Some pre-processing of the material is required • Limited resources due to land area requirements
Geothermal	• No pollutants produced • Uses naturally occurring hot water and steam directly • Low start-up costs	• Restricted to certain volcanic areas • Subsidence risk

Quick Test

1. What is a biofuel?
2. P2 Give one advantage and one disadvantage of solar power.

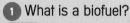

1. A 1200W hairdryer is used for 15 minutes. How many joules of energy are transferred? **[2]**

2. Calculate the height of a 160g ball if it has 30J of gravitational potential energy. (Use g = 10m/s².) **[2]**

3. A new theme park ride lifts its occupants vertically. It then drops them downwards under the influence of gravity.

   Assuming there is no energy loss as heat or sound, calculate the maximum velocity reached after the ride has dropped 30m. (Use g = 10m/s².) **[3]**

4 Why is electricity described as a secondary energy source? **[1]**

....

....

5 What is the purpose of a Sankey diagram? **[2]**

....

....

6 What useful energy change occurs in a wind turbine? **[1]**

7 Complete the table about the efficiency of electrical appliances. **[3]**

Electrical appliance	Energy in	Useful energy out	Efficiency
Iron	2000J/s	Heat: 1600J/s	
Radio	200J/s	Sound: 60J/s	
Computer	400J/s	Light: 180J/s Sound: 80J/s	

8 Calculate the efficiency of a coal-fired power station that uses 1500MW of power from coal to produce 555MW of electricity. **[1]**

....

Exam Practice Questions

9 Explain the following observations.

a) A carpet feels warmer to bare feet than a stone floor. [2]

b) Two thin blankets are usually warmer than one thick one. [2]

c) To escape a room filled with smoke, you should crawl on the floor. [2]

d) The element is at the bottom of an electric kettle. [2]

e) The cooling pipes on the back of a refrigerator are painted black. [2]

10 a) Calculate the efficiency of a light bulb that uses 100W of electrical energy to produce 8W of light energy. [2]

b) What happens to the rest of the energy supplied to the light bulb? [1]

c) What electrical power is used by a lamp that has an efficiency of 40% and a useful power output of 8W? [2]

11 A student bounces a ball. Each bounce reduces in height.

a) What kind of energy does the ball gain each time it moves up from the ground? **[1]**

b) The ball changes shape slightly each time it hits the ground. As it does so, energy is stored. What type of energy is this? **[1]**

c) What type of energy does the ball have when it is moving? **[1]**

d) Energy is transferred away from the ball each time it hits the ground. What observation tells you that this is the case? **[1]**

e) What happens to the air around the ball as it hits the ground? Explain your answer. **[2]**

12 **a)** State the equation which links gravitational potential energy, mass and height. **[1]**

b) A block of mass 9kg is lifted through a height of 8m. Calculate the gravitational potential energy gained by the block. **[2]**

Density and Pressure

Density

The **density** of a material is a measure of how 'squashed up' it is. A heavy object contains more mass than a light object of the same size.

Density is calculated using the formula:

$$\text{Density} = \frac{\text{Mass}}{\text{Volume}}$$

$$\text{or } \rho = \frac{M}{V}$$

where: m is mass in g or kg
v = volume in cm^3 or m^3
ρ = density in g/cm^3 or kg/m^3

You must use units consistently: either g and cm throughout or kg and m throughout. If the weight is given in N, then you must convert it to g or kg before using this equation.

Football (light object)

Bowling Ball (heavy object)

The Density of a Regularly Shaped Object

You can use the formula above to work out the density of a block.

If you are given the dimensions of the block, then you can use these to work out the volume of the block.

If you are also given the mass of the block, then you can calculate its density.

Example

A rectangular block has dimensions 10cm × 4.5cm × 6.5cm. Its weight is 11.2N. Find the density of the block.

$$\text{Mass} = \frac{11.2}{10} = 1.12\text{kg or } 1120\text{g}$$

Volume of block = 10 × 4.5 × 6.5 = 292.5cm^3

$$\text{Density} = \frac{1120}{292.5} = \textbf{3.83g/cm}^3 \text{ or } \textbf{3830kg/m}^3$$

The Density of an Irregularly Shaped Object

To find the density of an irregularly shaped object:
1. Find its mass.
2. Then submerge it in a measuring cylinder containing liquid.
3. Measure the difference in volume of the liquid with the object submerged in it and the volume of the liquid without the object submerged in it, as shown in the diagram.
4. The volume of the object is $V_2 - V_1$ and then the density can be calculated using $\text{Density} = \dfrac{\text{Mass}}{\text{Volume}}$

Volume V_1

Volume V_2

Pressure

This formula connects **pressure**, force and area:

> **Pressure** (Pascals) $= \dfrac{\textbf{Force (Newtons)}}{\textbf{Area (m}^2)}$

$1\ Pa = 1N/m^2$. Pressure can also be given in terms of bars, where 1 bar = 100 000Pa = 100kPa

Example

Calculate the pressure exerted when a force of 15N acts over an area of $0.5m^2$.

$$Pressure = \frac{15}{0.5} = 30N/m^2 = \textbf{30Pa}$$

Pressure in Fluids

Particles in a fluid or a gas are constantly moving. They constantly and randomly collide with each other and the walls of the container.

These collisions cause a force on the other particles and the walls of the container. This force is usually described in terms of the pressure it causes in a particular area.

The pressure at any point in a liquid or gas acts equally in all directions.

Atmospheric pressure is approximately 100kPa.

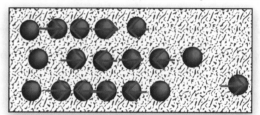

Pressure Difference, Height and Density

If you dive below the surface of water, the 'column' of water above you puts pressure on you. At a depth of 10m below the surface, the pressure increases by 100kPa. At 20m below the surface the pressure has increased by another 100kPa. This explains why scuba divers cannot dive more than 20m below the surface without extra safety precautions.

The increase in pressure below the surface of a liquid depends on the depth below the surface, h, and the density of the liquid, ρ. The pressure experienced at a depth, h, below the surface of a liquid, or between any two points in the liquid, is given by the equation:

> **Pressure difference $=$ Height $\times$ Density $\times$ Gravitational field strength**
> $$p = h \times \rho \times g$$
> where: p is the pressure difference in Pascals, h is the height in m, ρ is the density in kg/m^3, g is the gravitational field strength in N/Kg

The unit for pressure is Pa (N/m^2). Density must be in kg/m^3. If the density is given in g/cm^3 you must convert it to kg/m^3 before using it in the equation by multiplying by 1000.

Quick Test

1. What is the formula for finding density?
2. Calculate the density of a block which has a mass of 50g and where the change in volume when it is placed in a measuring cylinder of water is $25cm^3$.
3. Calculate the mass of a steel key that causes a change in volume in a measuring cylinder of $15cm^3$ (Density of steel = $7800kg/m^3$).
4. Calculate the pressure when a force of 26N acts over an area of $1.3m^2$.
5. Explain why pressure in a fluid acts equally in all directions.
6. Water has a density of $1000kg/m^3$. What is the pressure at a depth of 0.75m below the surface?

Change of State

P2 States of Matter

The three states of matter are **solid**, **liquid** and **gas**.

The table shows the arrangement of particles and the motion of particles in each of the three states.

Solid   Liquid   Gas

State	Arrangement of particles	Motion of particles
Solid	Regular pattern, closely packed together, particles held in place	Vibrate in place within the structure
Liquid	Irregular, closely packed together, particles able to move past each other	'Slide' over each other in a random motion
Gas	Irregular, widely spaced, particles able to move freely	Random motion, faster movement than the other states

P2 Melting and Boiling

If you heat ice in a thermally insulated beaker and plot a graph of temperature against time, you will obtain a graph like this.

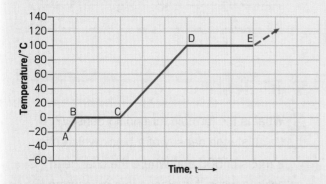

The ice is **melting** between points **B** and **C** on the graph. The energy from the heat source has gone into the beaker and the internal energy of the contents of the beaker has gone up, but the temperature has stayed the same. **The extra energy has been used to separate the particles in the ice to melt it, changing it from solid to liquid.**

From point **D** to point **E**, the particles are being given **enough energy to break away from the surface of the liquid** so the liquid starts to **boil**. (Note that condensation is the reverse of boiling and solidification is the reverse of melting.)

Evaporation

Evaporation occurs when particles break away from the surface of a liquid to form a vapour. The more energetic particles break away from the surface, as shown in the diagram.

This reduces the average energy of the molecules remaining in the liquid and so the liquid cools.

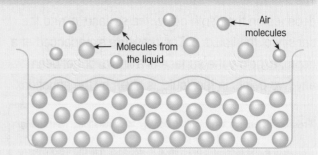

Quick Test

1. Draw diagrams to show the arrangement of particles in solids, liquids and gases.
2. Explain, with reference to energy of molecules, why evaporation of a liquid causes the liquid to cool.

Ideal Gas Molecules

Kinetic Theory of Gases

The **kinetic theory** of gases helps to build up a set of ideas from the basic idea that gases are made up of many tiny particles, called molecules. These ideas give a picture of what happens inside a gas.

Observed Feature of Gas	Related Ideas from Kinetic Theory
Gases have mass that can be measured	The total mass of a gas is the sum of the masses of the individual molecules
Gases have a temperature that can be measured	The individual molecules are always moving. The faster they move (the more kinetic energy they have), the higher the temperature of the gas
Gases have a pressure that can be measured	When the molecules hit the walls of the container, they exert a force on it. It is this force, divided by the surface area of the container, that is observed when measuring pressure
Gases have a volume that can be measured	Although the volume of each molecule is tiny, they are always moving about and spread out throughout the container
Temperature has an absolute zero	As temperature falls, the speed of the molecules (and their kinetic energy) becomes less. At absolute zero (−273°C) the molecules have stopped moving

Brownian Motion

Brownian motion is one of the observations that give evidence for the molecular model of matter. Small particles, such as pollen or fine smoke particles, can be seen through a microscope moving in a random way. The reason for this is that the particles are constantly being hit by even smaller particles, which are too small to see (e.g. water or air molecules).

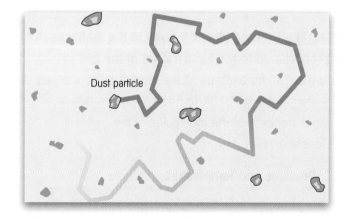

Dust particle

Absolute Zero

As a gas in a sealed container cools down, its molecules vibrate less, and move more slowly. If you keep cooling the gas down, there is a temperature at which all movement of the molecules has stopped. This temperature is known as **absolute zero** and is −273°C.

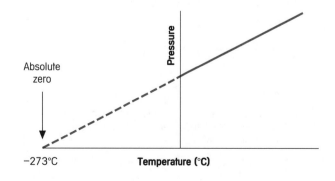

Ideal Gas Molecules

Kelvin Scale of Temperature

The existence of an absolute zero of temperature allows an alternative scale of temperature to be developed, in which absolute zero has the value 0. This scale of temperature is called the **Kelvin scale of temperature**. The steps in this scale are the same size as the steps on the Celsius scale, which means that it is easy to convert between the two scales by adding or subtracting 273. The scales are shown in this table.

Scale	Absolute Zero	Melting Point of Ice	Boiling Point of Water	Melting Point of Gold
Celsius	−273°C	0°C	100°C	1064°C
Kelvin	0K	273K	373K	1337K

To convert from degrees Celsius to kelvin, add 273.

To convert from kelvin to degrees Celsius, subtract 273.

The Gas Laws

Average Speed of Molecules and Temperature

Individual molecules of a gas are always moving, until the temperature reaches absolute zero. **The higher the temperature of the gas, the faster the molecules move, and the greater kinetic energy they have**.

Although all the molecules in a volume of gas are travelling at different speeds, it is possible to calculate the average speed of the molecules and hence their average kinetic energy. As temperature increases, the average speed of the gas molecules increases, and so the average kinetic energy increases.

(P2) **The average kinetic energy of the molecules is proportional to the temperature of the gas in kelvin**. So, for example, if the temperature of a gas is doubled from 273K to 546K, then the average kinetic energy of the molecules of the gas will double as well.

Pressure and Temperature

The **pressure** in a sealed container **increases as the temperature goes up**. Using the kelvin scale, the pressure is proportional to the temperature. So if the pressure doubles, the temperature also doubles.

This is written mathematically as:

$$p \propto T$$
$$p = kT$$

where: p is the pressure in Pascals, T is the temperature in kelvin and k is a constant that depends on the size of the container and the amount of gas in it

If you are given initial and final pressures and temperatures for a gas at constant volume, use the equation: $\dfrac{p_1}{T_1} = \dfrac{p_2}{T_2}$

where p_1 and p_2 are the initial and final pressures respectively, and T_1 and T_2 are the initial and final temperatures respectively.

Example

A tyre is filled to a pressure of 2.5 bar at a temperature of 20°C. After a long journey the tyre reaches a temperature of 50°C. What is the pressure now?

Convert temperatures to kelvin and substitute values into the equation:

$$\frac{2.5}{293} \times 323 = \textbf{2.76 bar}$$

Key Words   **Kelvin scale of temperature**

The Gas Laws (Cont.)

Pressure and Volume

The more you push the piston of the bicycle pump shown with the outlet blocked, the harder it is to push in. This is because the pressure in the container goes up.

piston moved in

The molecular model of gases says that there is the same number of molecules in the container travelling at the same speed. However, as the volume is reduced, the molecules are packed more densely and so there will be more collisions with the walls and with the piston per second.

If the volume is halved, the number of collisions will double, and **the pressure on the piston will double**. This law is often called Boyle's law, and **only applies if the temperature of the gas does not change**.

A fixed volume of gas in a sealed container obeys the following equation:

Pressure × Volume ═ Constant
$$pV \equiv \text{Constant}$$
where: p is pressure in Pa
V is volume in m^3

In a question, you can write that the initial pressure and volume multiplied together are constant:
p_1V_1 = constant

Similarly, the final pressure and volume multiplied together are constant: **p_2V_2 = constant**

The constant is the same in both cases, so **$p_1V_1 = p_2V_2$**

This equation can be used **as long as the temperature is constant**.

Example

A bicycle pump contains 300cm³ of air at atmospheric pressure. The air is compressed slowly. What is the pressure when the volume of air is 150cm³?
(Atmospheric pressure = 100kPa)

Substitute the values into the equation:

$$300 \times 100 = p_2 \times 150$$

$$p_2 = \frac{30\ 000}{150}$$

$$p_2 = \textbf{200kPa}$$

Quick Test

1. Using ideas from kinetic theory, explain why gases in a container have a pressure that can be measured.
2. Explain why Brownian motion is supporting evidence for particle theory.
3. Why is there an absolute zero of temperature, −273°C?
4. What is the melting point of ice in the kelvin scale of temperature?
5. Water in a bath is at 65°C. What is this temperature in kelvin?
6. What is the relationship between the temperature of a gas and the average speed of its molecules?
7. What happens to the pressure of a gas in a sealed container as the temperature goes up?
8. What happens to the pressure of a gas in a sealed container if the volume is doubled?
9. The volume of an inflated balloon is 1450cm³ at a pressure of 100kPa. Find the volume of the balloon at a pressure of 50kPa.

1 A student is investigating the density of a liquid.

The student uses scales that measure mass to the nearest gram and a measuring cylinder that is marked with volume in cm³.

The student finds the mass of the measuring cylinder by putting the empty measuring cylinder on the scales.

Then the student puts some liquid into the measuring cylinder and finds the mass of the measuring cylinder and the liquid.

Finally, the student finds the volume of liquid in the measuring cylinder.

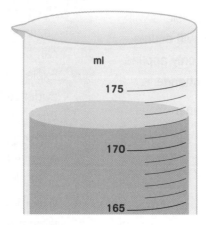

a) i) What is the mass of the liquid in the cylinder? **[2]**

ii) What is the volume of the liquid? **[1]**

b) What is the density of the liquid? **[2]**

P2 2 **a)** Draw a diagram to show the particle arrangements in **i)** a solid **ii)** a liquid **iii)** a gas. **[3]**

b) State how the particles move in a liquid. **[1]**

c) Name the process which occurs when a liquid changes to a gas. **[1]**

3 There are two identical cups on a table. One is full of tea and the other is half full.

Explain why the pressure on a sugar lump at the bottom of each cup is different. **[4]**

4 **a)** A diver is exploring a wreck. As he dives lower below the surface of the water, the pressure on him increases.

    i) State the equation that is used to find the pressure exerted on the diver at a given depth. **[1]**

    ii) The diver starts at a depth of 25m and then sees an object that he wants to investigate at a depth of 145m. Calculate the increase in pressure he experiences. (The density of sea water is 1025kg/m³.) **[3]**

    iii) The water is stationary above the diver. In what direction does the pressure act on the diver? **[1]**

b) Everyone on Earth experiences a pressure. Explain what causes this pressure. **[2]**

5 **a)** A kettle boils at 100°C and steam is observed coming out of the spout of the kettle.

    i) What is 100°C in kelvin? **[1]**

    ii) State one way in which the molecules in water are different from the molecules in steam. **[1]**

b) Use the kinetic theory of matter to explain how molecules of steam exert a pressure on the inside of the kettle. **[4]**

P2 **c)** A gas cylinder is used to heat a pan of water. 850cm³ of gas, at a pressure of 120kPa, escapes from the gas cylinder. As the gas escapes, its pressure decreases to 101kPa.

Calculate the volume of the escaped gas at the new pressure. **[2]**

d) The cylinder is turned off so that gas can no longer escape. The temperature of the gas in the cylinder decreases. Explain what happens to the pressure of the gas in the cylinder. **[2]**

Magnetism

P2 Magnets Repel and Attract

If a permanent magnet is suspended and allowed to swing, it will line up approximately north–south. The two ends of the magnet (the most strongly magnetic parts) are called the north pole and the south pole (often labelled N and S). Note that they are actually north-seeking and south-seeking poles.

Like poles from two different magnets will **repel** each other. **Unlike poles** from two different magnets will **attract** each other.

Magnets will also **attract** some materials, which are called **magnetic materials**. Several elements are magnetic. Examples are iron, cobalt and nickel. Alloys have been developed which are also magnetic.

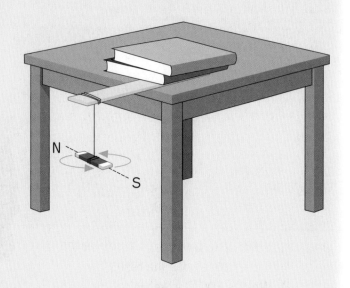

P2 Magnetically Hard and Soft Materials

Materials that stay magnetic once they have been magnetised are called **magnetically hard** materials. (When we call something a magnet, we mean a permanent magnet that is made of magnetically hard material.)

There are some **materials which do not stay magnetic** once they have been magnetised. These materials are called **magnetically soft** materials. These materials are particularly useful in devices such as electromagnets.

It is important to realise that the terms 'magnetically hard' and 'magnetically soft' refer to a material's magnetic behaviour, and not to its physical hardness or softness. It is possible to get a physically soft, magnetically hard material. These are often found in rubberised magnetic strips used on notice boards.

P2 Magnetic Induction

If a soft magnetic material is brought near to a magnet, it will be attracted. It will have magnetism **induced** in it and will become **magnetised**. When the magnet is taken away, the material will lose its magnetism. Note that the magnet will continue to attract the soft magnetic material even if the material is turned round.

This is the opposite behaviour to two magnets. One pole of a magnet will repel another magnet. This enables you to work out whether you are holding two magnets, or one magnet and one piece of soft magnetic material.

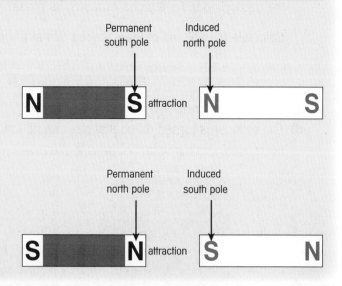

Magnetic Fields

Magnets have a **magnetic field** around them. This is a region of space where their magnetism affects other objects. Magnetic fields are visualised using **magnetic field lines**. These lines show the path that a free north pole would take from a north pole to a south pole. The closer together the field lines are, the stronger the magnetic field.

Investigating Magnetic Fields

You can investigate the magnetic field around a bar magnet by placing the magnet under a thin sheet of plastic and then sprinkling iron filings over the plastic. The diagram shows the result.

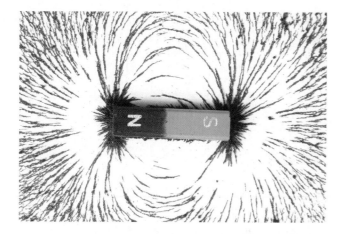

You can use a similar technique to investigate the field pattern between two magnets. The diagram shows the results for different arrangements.

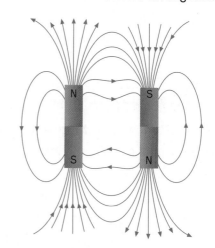

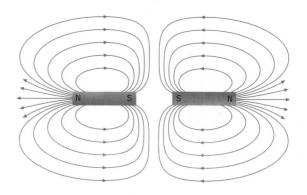

Uniform Magnetic Fields

A uniform magnetic field can be produced by placing two bar magnets with the north pole of one very close to the south pole of another. The field between the poles will be uniform. You can get the same result using a single bar magnet that has been bent into a U-shape, as shown in the diagram.

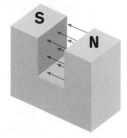

Quick Test

1. What happens when a south-seeking pole of one magnet is brought close to a south-seeking pole of another magnet?
2. What does it mean to say that a material is magnetically hard?
3. How can you decide whether you have two magnets, or one magnet and one piece of soft magnetic material?
4. What is a magnetic field?
5. What is a magnetic field line?

Electromagnetism

Magnetic Field around a Wire

A straight wire carrying an electric current has a circular **magnetic field** around it. The magnetic field is made up of **concentric circles**.

If the wire is put near a magnet, the two magnetic fields interact and the wire can move.

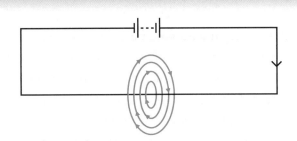

(P2) Magnetic Field around Coils

The magnetic field around a **rectangular coil** forms straight lines through the centre of the coil:

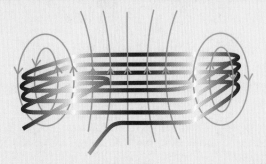

A coil of wire is known as a solenoid. The magnetic field around a **solenoid** looks like the magnetic field around a bar magnet:

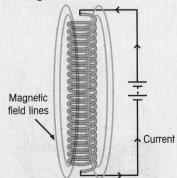

Magnetic field lines

Current

(P2) Charged Particles Moving in a Magnetic Field

A current is a flow of charged particles. If a current-carrying wire is placed in a magnetic field it experiences a force and moves. This is called the **motor effect**.

For a current-carrying wire in a magnetic field to experience the maximum **force**, it has to be at **right angles** to the magnetic field.

The direction the wire moves in depends upon:
- the direction of the current
- the direction of the magnetic field.

The direction the wire moves in can be reversed by:
- reversing the direction of the current
- reversing the direction of the magnetic field.

Fleming's Left-Hand Rule

Fleming's left-hand rule can be used to predict the direction of the force on a current-carrying wire.

The rule states that if:
- your first finger points in the direction of the magnetic field, N to S, **and**
- your second finger points in the direction of the current, + to –, **then**
- your thumb will point in the direction of the force on the wire.

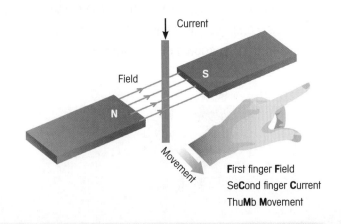

Current

Field

S

N

Movement

First finger **F**ield
Se**C**ond finger **C**urrent
Thu**M**b **M**ovement

P2 The Construction of Electromagnets

An electromagnet is a piece of wire that has a magnetic field around it when an electric current flows through it. When the current is switched off, the magnetic field is not present.

If a current flows through a solenoid it behaves like a bar magnet. If a magnetically soft core is placed in the centre of the coil, when the coil is magnetised the core is magnetised too. This makes the magnetic field around the coil much stronger.

P2 Field Lines around Electromagnets

A straight wire has a circular magnetic field around it, as shown in the diagram. The dot indicates that the current is travelling out of the page; the cross indicates that the current is travelling into the page.

The magnetic field around a solenoid is as shown in the diagram.

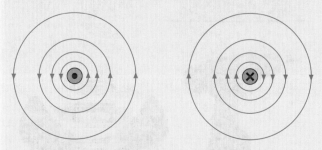

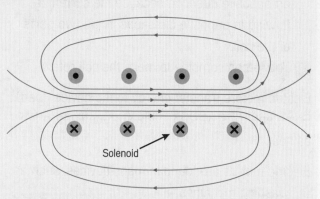

Solenoid

The magnetic field around a flat circular coil is as shown in the diagram.

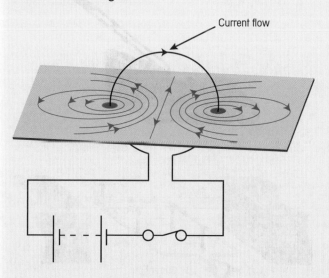

Current flow

Quick Test

1. Describe the magnetic field around a rectangular coil.
2. What happens if a charged particle moves in a magnetic field (not parallel to the magnetic field)?
3. State two ways in which the direction of motion of a current-carrying wire in a magnetic field can be reversed.
4. Is the magnetic field around an electromagnet always present? Explain your answer.
5. Sketch the magnetic field of a solenoid.

Electromagnetism

The Motor Effect

A simple **direct current** (**d.c.**) electric **motor** works by using a current-carrying coil.

When a current-carrying coil is placed in a magnetic field, it will **rotate** in the following way:

1. The current flowing through the coil creates a magnetic field.
2. The magnetic field of the magnet and the magnetic field of the coil interact.
3. Each side of the coil experiences a force in an opposite direction because the current is flowing in opposite directions in the two parts of the coil.
4. The forces combine to make the coil rotate.

Electric motors transfer energy to the device (load). Some energy is wasted to the surroundings, often as heat.

Electric motors are found in many devices, such as:

- washing machines
- CD players
- food processors
- electric drills and electric lawnmowers
- windscreen wipers.

Creating a Current

Changing the Motor Effect

The speed of a motor can be increased by:

- increasing the size of the electric current
- increasing the number of turns on the coil
- increasing the strength of the magnetic field.

The direction of the current affects the direction of the force on the motor coil.

The current must always flow in the same direction relative to the magnet in order to keep the coil rotating.

This is achieved by using a **split-ring commutator**. A split-ring commutator changes the direction of the current in the coil every half turn.

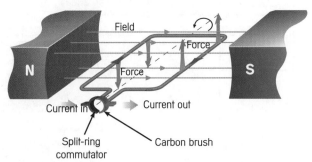

Field

Force

Force

N

S

Current in

Current out

Split-ring commutator

Carbon brush

Loudspeakers

The principle of the motor effect is also used in loudspeakers.

1. The coil is attached to a paper cone.
2. The changing current in the coil produces a changing magnetic field which interacts with the field from the permanent magnet.
3. This creates a backwards and forwards motion of the coil and paper cone.
4. This makes the air vibrate – a sound wave.

Magnet cut away to show central pole

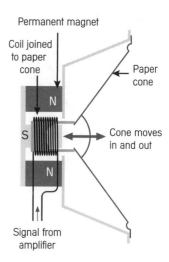

Permanent magnet

Coil joined to paper cone

Paper cone

Cone moves in and out

Signal from amplifier

Factors that Affect the Strength of the Magnetic Field

The size of the force on a current-carrying conductor in a magnetic field can be increased in the following ways.

1. Increase the **size of the current** (e.g. have more cells).
2. Increase the **strength of the magnetic field** (e.g. have stronger magnets).

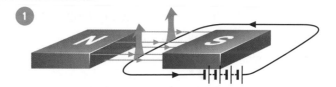
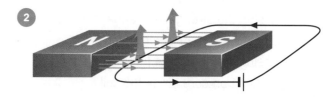

Quick Test

1. Explain the operation of a d.c. motor.
2. Explain the functioning of a loudspeaker.
3. Explain how the size of the force on a current-carrying conductor can be decreased.

Electromagnetic Induction

Inducing Voltage

When a magnet is moved into a coil of wire, a **voltage** is induced between the ends of the wire because the **magnetic field** is being cut.

If the ends of the coil are connected to make a complete circuit, a **current** will be induced. This is called **electromagnetic induction**.

Moving the magnet into the coil induces a current in one direction. You can then induce a current in the opposite direction by:
- moving the magnet out of the coil
- moving the other pole of the magnet into the coil.

If there's no movement of the coil or magnet, there's no induced current.

Moving the Magnet into the Coil

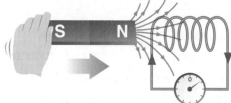

Moving the Magnet out of the Coil

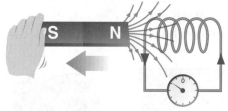

Moving the Other Pole of the Magnet into the Coil

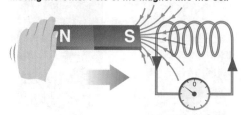

The Electric Generator

Mains electricity is produced by **generators**.

Generators use the principle of **electromagnetic induction** to generate electricity by rotating a magnet inside a coil.

The size of the induced voltage can be increased by:
- increasing the speed of rotation of the magnet
- increasing the strength of the magnetic field, possibly by using an electromagnet
- increasing the number of turns on the coil
- placing an iron core inside the coil.

As the magnet rotates, the **voltage** induced in the coil changes direction and size, as shown in the diagram. The **current** that's produced is an **alternating current** as it reverses its direction of flow every half turn of the magnet. The direction of the voltage and current after one full turn of the magnet are in the same direction as they were at the start, before the magnet was turned.

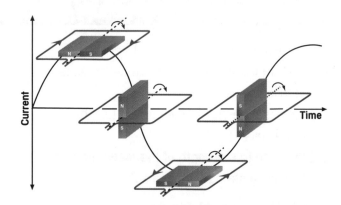

Quick Test

1. Why is a voltage induced between the ends of a coil of wire if a magnet is moved into the coil?
2. What happens if the coil and magnet do not move relative to each other?
3. How can the size of the induced voltage be increased?

Key Words   **Generator**

P2 Transformers

A **transformer** changes electrical energy from one potential difference to another potential difference.

Transformers are made up of two coils, called the **primary** and **secondary coils**, wrapped around a soft iron core.

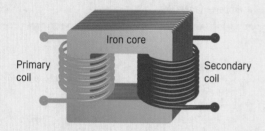

An **alternating potential difference** across the primary coil causes an **alternating current** to flow (input).

This alternating current creates a continuously changing magnetic field in the iron core, which induces an **alternating potential difference** across the ends of the secondary coil (output).

The **potential difference** across the primary and secondary coils of a transformer are related by the equation:

$$\frac{V_p}{V_s} = \frac{n_p}{n_s}$$

where: V_p is the potential difference across the primary coil in volts (V), V_s is the potential difference across the secondary coil in volts (V), n_p is the number of turns on the primary coil and n_s is the number of turns on the secondary coil

For example, a transformer has 200 turns on the primary coil and 800 turns on the secondary coil.

If a potential difference of 230V is applied to the primary coil, the potential difference across the secondary coil can be determined using the equation above.

$$\frac{230}{V_s} = \frac{200}{800}$$

$$V_s = 920V$$

Step-up and Step-down Transformers

A **step-up transformer** has more turns in the secondary coil than the primary coil. The potential difference across the secondary coil is **greater** than that across the primary coil.

A **step-down transformer** has fewer turns in the secondary coil than the primary coil. The potential difference across the secondary coil is less than that across the primary coil.

Step-up and step-down transformers are used in the large-scale transmission of electricity to ensure the efficient transmission of electricity.

A Step-up Transformer

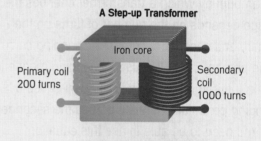

A Step-down Transformer

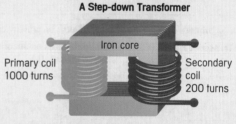

When overhead power cables carry current they get hot, so energy is wasted as heat. This power loss can be reduced by reducing the current. The power loss in transmission relates to the current **squared**.

Power loss = (Current²) ✕ Resistance
where: power loss is measured in watts, current is in amperes (amps) and resistance is in ohms

In a step-up transformer, if the voltage is increased, the current automatically decreases. So, they are used to increase the voltages from power stations.

Step-down transformers are used in substations to reduce the voltages for domestic and commercial users.

Electromagnetic Induction

P2 Transformer Efficiency

If transformers were assumed to be 100% efficient, the electrical power output would equal the electrical power input.

This can be stated using the equation:

$$V_p \times I_p = V_s \times I_s$$

where: V_p is the potential difference across the primary coil in volts (V), and I_p is the current in the primary coil in amperes (amps, A), and V_s is the potential difference across the secondary coil in volts (V), and I_s is the current in the secondary coil in amperes (amps, A)

P2 The Relationship Between Input and Output Voltage and Number of Turns on Each Coil

The amount by which a transformer changes the voltage depends on the number of turns on the primary and secondary coils. The changing current in the primary coil will cause a changing magnetic field in the iron core, which in turn will cause a changing potential difference across the secondary coil. You need to be able to use this equation:

$$\frac{\text{Voltage on primary coil } (V_p)}{\text{Voltage on secondary coil } (V_s)} = \frac{\text{Number of turns on primary coil } (N_p)}{\text{Number of turns on secondary coil } (N_s)}$$

Quick Test

1. What are the main components of a transformer?
2. Do transformers use a direct current or an alternating current?
3. If a current of 0.3 amps is supplied to a transformer in a laptop at a voltage of 230 volts, what current is fed to the laptop after the voltage has been stepped down to 12 volts?
4. A transformer has a primary coil of 200 turns. If the transformer changes 12V to 240V, how many turns must be on the secondary coil?

Example 1

A transformer has 1000 turns on the primary coil and 200 turns on the secondary coil. If a voltage of 250V is applied to the primary coil, what is the voltage across the secondary coil?

$$\frac{250}{V_s} = \frac{1000}{200}$$

$$250 = 5V_s \text{ so } V_s = \frac{250}{5} = \textbf{50V}$$

Example 2

A laptop runs on 12V. If it's to be plugged into the mains (230V), a transformer is needed. If the transformer has 960 turns on the primary coil, how many turns does it have on the secondary coil?

$$\frac{V_p}{V_s} = \frac{N_p}{N_s}$$

$$N_s = \frac{N_p \times V_s}{V_p}$$

$$N_s = \frac{960 \times 12}{230}$$

$$= \textbf{50 turns}$$

1 The diagram below shows a coil of wire located between the poles of a magnet.

The arrows indicate the direction of the conventional current.

a) On the diagram draw arrows to show the direction of the force on sides X and Y on the coil of wire. **[2]**

b) What rule is used to determine this direction? **[1]**

c) Explain why these forces cause the coil to rotate. **[2]**

d) What is the name given to this effect? **[1]**

e) What would happen to the coil if the magnets were swapped around? **[1]**

f) What two methods could be used to allow the coil to rotate faster about its axle? **[2]**

2 Give two ways to increase the size of an induced voltage in a generator. **[2]**

3 Chevelle was experimenting by moving a magnet into a coil of wire that was connected to an ammeter. She noticed that the ammeter showed a current flowing in one direction.

Four students are discussing how she could reverse the direction of the current.

Jessie
I would move the magnet into the coil more quickly.

Sonny
Try using a coil with more turns on it.

Jake
You could move the magnet out of the coil.

Shanika
Just rotate the magnet through 180° then move it out of the coil.

a) Which student gave the correct way to reverse the current? Put a tick (✓) in the box next to the correct name. **[1]**

Jessie ⬡   Sonny ⬡   Jake ⬡   Shanika ⬡

b) Which **two** students gave a way to increase the current? Put ticks (✓) in the boxes next to the two correct names. **[1]**

Jessie ⬡   Sonny ⬡   Jake ⬡   Shanika ⬡

P2 **4** Explain how, when an alternating potential difference is applied across a primary coil of a transformer, it's possible to obtain an alternating potential difference of a higher value across the secondary coil. **[6]**

....

....

....

....

....

5 A transformer has a primary coil of 3000 turns and is connected to a 150V alternating supply. If the output voltage is 900V, how many turns are there on the secondary coil? **[1]**

....

....

6 Students used this circuit to investigate a simple electric motor.

a) State why the coil of the motor spins when the switch is closed. **[2]**

....

....

....

....

b) State two ways to make the coil of the motor spin more slowly. **[2]**

....

....

c) The students changed the circuit by replacing the cell and switch with a lamp.

The students spin the coil of the motor by hand. The lamp lights. Explain why this happens. **[2]**

....

....

....

7 a) Describe how you would use the equipment shown in the diagram to investigate the magnetic field around the bar magnet. **[3]**

....

....

....

....

b) Draw the magnetic field pattern for the bar magnet shown. **[2]**

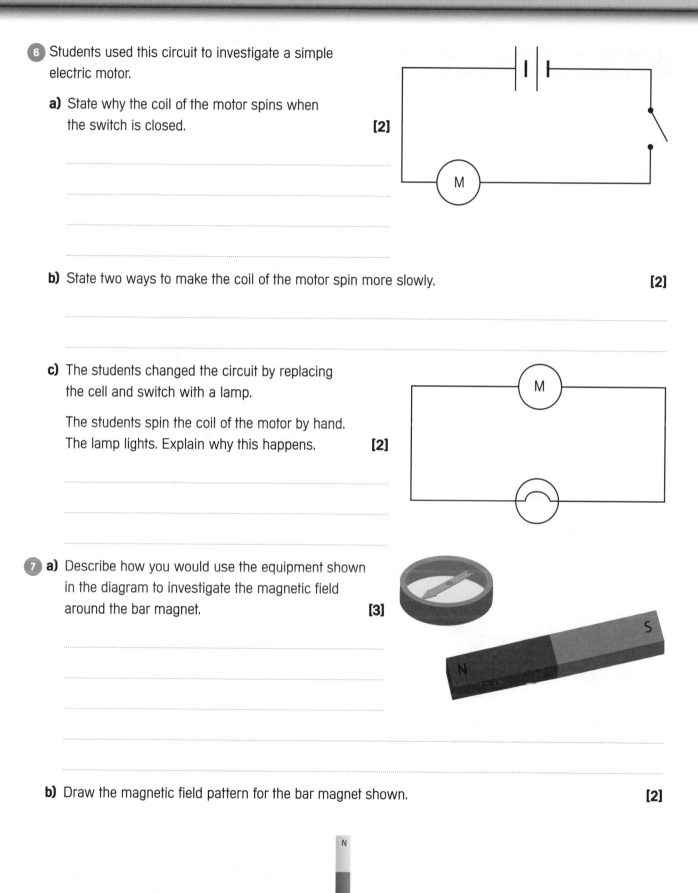

Particles

Atomic Structure

Atoms are the basic particles from which all matter is made. The basic structure of an **atom** is an extremely tiny central nucleus composed of **protons** (positive charge) and **neutrons** (no electrical charge) surrounded by **electrons** (negative charge).

This model of the atom, the nuclear model, was based on results from the Rutherford and Marsden scattering experiments and replaced the earlier 'plum pudding model'.

A Fluorine Atom

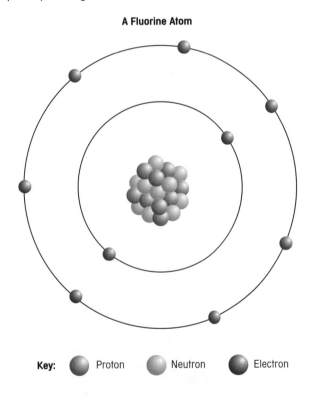

Key: ● Proton ● Neutron ● Electron

In an atom the number of **electrons** is equal to the number of **protons** in the nucleus. So the atom as a whole has no electrical charge and is therefore electrically **neutral**. In the nuclear model most of the atom is empty space.

Atoms of different elements have different numbers of protons (and electrons).

The number of protons in an atom therefore defines the element.

- The number of **protons** in an atom is called its **atomic number**.
- The number of **protons and neutrons** in an atom is called its **mass number** (protons and neutrons are collectively called nucleons).

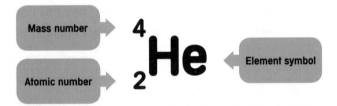

Mass number → ^{4}

Atomic number → $_{2}$ He ← Element symbol

Atomic Particle	Relative Mass	Relative Charge
Proton	1	+1
Neutron	1	0
Electron	$\frac{1}{2000}$	−1

The size of the nucleus is about 10^5 times smaller than the size of the atom.

Isotopes and Ions

Some atoms of the **same element** can have different numbers of **neutrons**. These are called **isotopes**.

For example, oxygen has three common isotopes: $^{16}_{8}O$, $^{17}_{8}O$, $^{18}_{8}O$, with only $^{16}_{8}O$ being stable.

Atoms may also lose or gain electrons to form charged particles called **ions**. An atom that has gained electrons is called a **negative ion**. An atom that has lost electrons is a **positive ion**. Positively

charged ions attract negatively charged ions and can form a strong bond, e.g. sodium chloride (salt).

Quick Test

1. Describe the basic structure of an atom.
2. What is the atomic number?
3. What is the mass number?

Key Words   Atom • Proton • Neutron • Atomic number • Mass number • Isotopes • Ion

Unstable Nuclei

Isotopes of atoms that have too many or too few neutrons form **unstable nuclei**. The nuclei may disintegrate by **randomly emitting ionising radiation**. Atoms of these isotopes are **radioactive** (also called **radioactive** isotopes, radioisotopes or radionuclides). The process of disintegration is called **radioactive decay**.

Radioactive Decay

The radioactive decay process can result in the formation of a different atom with a different number of protons. Three examples of this decay process are:

- **alpha radiation (α)**
- **beta radiation (β)**
- **gamma radiation (γ)**.

Unlike alpha and beta decay, gamma emissions have no effect on the internal structure of the nucleus. Gamma radiation is a form of electromagnetic radiation that carries away any surplus energy from the nucleus. Gamma radiation can be used, for example, in radiotherapy to kill cancer cells and shrink malignant tumours.

Radiation can cause damage to living cells. Inside the body alpha radiation is most dangerous as it is easily absorbed by cells, whereas beta and gamma radiation are less harmful as they easily pass though the cells. Outside the body the roles are reversed, with alpha radiation less harmful and beta and gamma considerably more dangerous.

Alpha Decay

In alpha decay the original atom decays by ejecting an **alpha particle** from its nucleus.

An alpha particle is a huge particle. It's identical to a **helium nucleus**, consisting of **two protons** and **two neutrons**, and symbolised by ^4_2He. In alpha decay a completely new atom is formed.

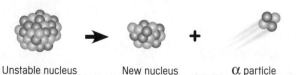

Unstable nucleus   New nucleus α particle

For example, Radium-226 decays by alpha emission to form Radon-222, a radioactive gas. The nuclear equation for this decay process is:

$$^{226}_{88}\text{Ra} \longrightarrow {}^{222}_{86}\text{Rn} + {}^{4}_{2}\text{He}$$

Beta Decay

In beta decay the original atom decays by changing a **neutron** into a **proton** and an **electron** or by changing a **proton** into a **neutron** and a **positive electron** called a positron.

The newly formed high-energy electron is ejected from the nucleus. To distinguish it from orbiting electrons around an atom, the electron emitted is called a **beta particle**, with the symbol β.

Unstable nucleus   New nucleus β particle

For example, Radon-222 also decays by alpha emission to give Polonium-218. This new atom is also radioactive and decays by beta emission to give Astatine-218. The nuclear equation for this decay is:

$$^{218}_{84}\text{Po} \longrightarrow {}^{218}_{85}\text{At} + {}^{0}_{-1}\beta$$

Notice how the top and bottom numbers balance on either side of the equation. The beta particle in the above reaction carries a negative charge; in other reactions it carries a positive charge ($^{0}_{+1}\beta$).

Beta$^+$ decay (using positive electrons) is used in medical imaging (PET scans) as tracers to highlight and diagnose cancers.

Particles

Ionisation and Penetration Power

When radiation collides with **neutral** atoms or molecules in a substance, the atoms or molecules may become charged due to electrons (the outer electrons surrounding the atoms or molecules) being 'knocked out' of the orbiting structure during the collision.

This alters their structure, leaving the atoms or molecules as **ions** (i.e. atoms with an electrical charge) or as **charged particles**.

Each type of emitted radiation (alpha, beta, gamma) has a different:

- degree of **ionising power**
- ability to **penetrate** materials
- **range** in air
- amount of **deflection** in electric and magnetic fields.

The degree of deflection depends on:

- the **relative masses** of the alpha particle compared to the beta particle
- the **charge** on each particle (+2 for alpha particle and −1 for the beta particle).

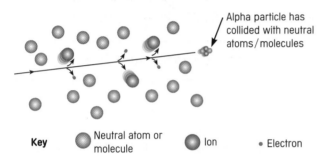

Alpha particle has collided with neutral atoms / molecules

Key   Neutral atom or molecule   Ion   • Electron

Particle	Description	Ionising Power	Penetration	Affected by Electric and Magnetic Fields
Alpha (α)	• Helium nucleus • Positive particle	Strong	Stopped by paper or skin or 6cm of air	Yes, but in the opposite direction to beta particles
Beta (β)	• Negative electron	Weak	Stopped by 3mm of aluminium	Yes, bent strongly, but opposite to alpha particles
Gamma (γ)	• Electromagnetic radiation • Very short wavelength	Very weak	Reduced but not stopped by lead	No

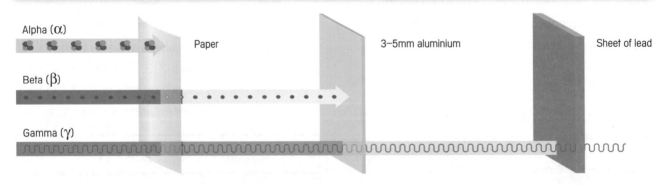

Alpha (α)   Paper   3–5mm aluminium   Sheet of lead

Beta (β)

Gamma (γ)

Quick Test

1. List the three types of ionising radiations.
2. Which ionising radiation will be stopped by a sheet of paper?
3. What is the effect on a nucleus of the emission of an alpha particle?

Detection of Ionising Radiation

Ionising radiation is invisible to the naked eye, but it affects photographic plates, e.g. X rays. Individual particles of radiation can be detected using a Geiger–Muller tube.

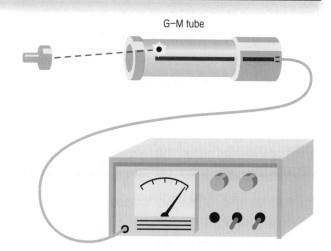

G–M tube

Background Radiation

Radioactive decay is all around us and is commonly referred to as **background radiation**.

Background radiation is **not harmful** to our health as it occurs in very small amounts or radiation doses. Actual levels depend on where you live and what occupation you have.

Sources of background radiation can be divided into those that are natural and those that are man-made.

The following are some sources of background radiation:

* Cosmic rays
* Radiation from rocks
* Radon gas
* Radioactive isotopes in the body
* Medical sources
* Consumer products
* Others (including air travel and occupational hazards).

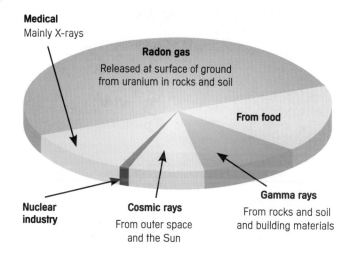

Medical
Mainly X-rays

Radon gas
Released at surface of ground from uranium in rocks and soil

From food

Nuclear industry

Cosmic rays
From outer space and the Sun

Gamma rays
From rocks and soil and building materials

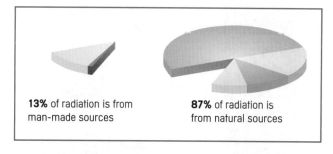

13% of radiation is from man-made sources

87% of radiation is from natural sources

Quick Test

1. How can ionising radiation be detected?
2. Name some sources of background radiation.

Radioactivity

Activity

The **activity** of a radioactive source is the number of ionising particles it emits each second. Over time, fewer particles are left to decay so the activity drops. Activity is measured in becquerels (Bq).

Half-life

The **half-life** of a radioactive isotope is a measurement of the time it takes for the rate of decay (count rate) to halve **or** the time required for half of the original population of radioactive atoms to decay.

A radioactive isotope that has a very long half-life remains active for a very long time.

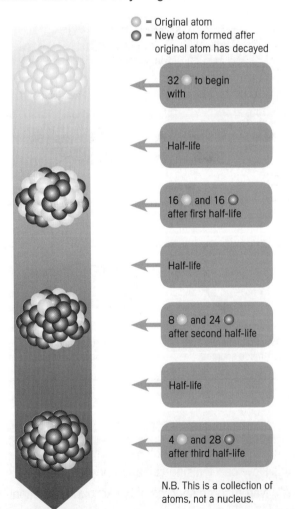

○ = Original atom
● = New atom formed after original atom has decayed

32 ● to begin with

Half-life

16 ● and 16 ○ after first half-life

Half-life

8 ● and 24 ○ after second half-life

Half-life

4 ● and 28 ○ after third half-life

N.B. This is a collection of atoms, not a nucleus.

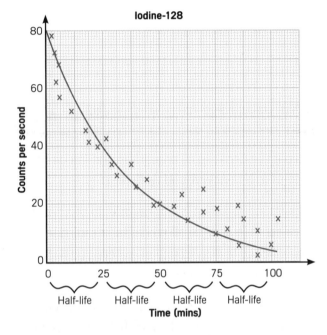

Iodine-128

The graph shows the count rate (using a Geiger counter) from a sample of radioactive Iodine-128 against time. It shows that:

* the initial count rate is 80 counts per second
* after 25 minutes (1 half-life) the count rate has fallen to 40 counts per second
* after two half-lives the count rate is only 20 counts per second.

Radioactive isotopes can have half-lives between fractions of a second to tens of thousands of years.

The choice of which radioisotope to use depends on its purpose and whether it is used internally or externally to diagnose or to treat.

Calculations with Half-life

Half-life can be calculated using a table or a graph.

Example 1

The table shows the activity of a radioactive substance against time.

Time (min)	Activity (Bq)
0	200
5	160
10	124
15	100
20	80
25	62
30	50

Calculate the half-life of the substance by:

a) using a table

b) drawing a graph.

a) Find an average by choosing three pairs of points between which the activity has halved.

Activity	Time	Half-life
200 → 100	0 → 15	15 min
160 → 80	5 → 20	15 min
100 → 50	15 → 30	15 min

The half-life is **15 minutes.**

b)

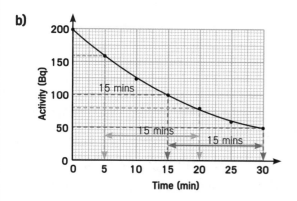

The half-life is **15 minutes**.

Example 2

The half-life of uranium-235 is 700 000 000 years. Uranium forms lead when it decays.

A sample is found to contain three times as much lead as uranium.

Calculate the age of the sample.

> Fraction of lead present is $\frac{3}{4}$. Fraction of uranium present is $\frac{1}{4}$

Fraction of lead ($\frac{3}{4}$) + Fraction of uranium ($\frac{1}{4}$) = Original amount of uranium (1)

> Work out the number of decays it takes to get to $\frac{1}{4}$

$$1 \xrightarrow{\text{half-life}} \frac{1}{2} \xrightarrow{\text{half-life}} \frac{1}{4} \quad \text{2 half-lives}$$

Age of rock = 2 × half-life

= 2 × 700 000 000 years

= **1 400 000 000 years**

Quick Test

1. How does the activity of a radioactive source change over time? Explain your answer.
2. What is the half-life of a radioisotope?
3. Is the value of the half-life the same for all radioisotopes?
4. The initial count rate from a radioactive sample is 100 counts per second. It has fallen to 25 counts per second after 16 minutes. What is the half-life of the sample?
5. The activity of a sample has fallen to $\frac{1}{8}$ of its initial value after 3 days. What is the half-life of the isotope?

Radioactivity

Dangers of Radiation

Ionising radiation can break molecules into ions.

These ions can damage living cells and the cells may be killed or become cancerous.

Ions are **very reactive** and can take part in other chemical reactions.

Many jobs involve using radioactive materials (e.g. workers in nuclear power stations, radiographers, etc.). People can become **irradiated** or **contaminated**, so their exposure needs to be carefully monitored.

Different types of radiation carry different risks:
- **Alpha** is the most dangerous if the source is **inside the body**; all the radiation will be absorbed by cells in the body.
- **Beta** is the most dangerous if the source is **outside the body**. Unlike alpha, it can penetrate the outer layer of skin and damage internal organs.
- **Gamma** can cause harm if it's absorbed by the cells, but it is weakly ionising and can pass straight through the body causing no damage at all.

The **sievert** is a measure of a radiation dose's potential to harm a person. It's based on both the type and the amount of radiation absorbed.

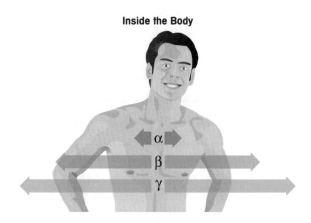

Inside the Body

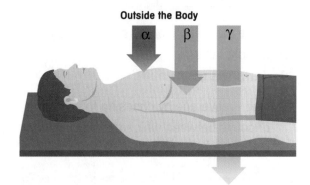

Outside the Body

Uses of Radiation

Although using ionising radiation can be dangerous, there are many beneficial uses.

High-energy gamma rays in **cancer treatment** can destroy cancer cells but can damage healthy cells too. The radiation has to be carefully targeted from different angles to minimise the damage. Doctors need to carefully weigh the **risks** against the benefits before going ahead.

Radiation is also used:
- to **sterilise surgical instruments** and to **sterilise food** – this kills bacteria
- to date archaeological specimens and rocks (the proportion of ^{14}C present falls over time)
- as a tracer in the body, for example in **PET** (**Positron Emission Tomography**) scans.

In PET scans, radio-labelled glucose is injected into the patient's bloodstream, from which it is absorbed into the tissues, as glucose is needed for respiration. A pair of gamma ray photons is emitted from the radio-labelled glucose in active cells. These are detected by gamma ray cameras and used to produce an image, for instance of the brain, showing any abnormal regions. Cancerous cells often absorb more glucose, so they will emit more gamma rays than surrounding tissues and will be detected.

In radiotherapy, a beam of gamma rays is focused from different angles onto cancer cells to destroy them. This gives a concentrated dose to the cancer cells but a smaller dose to the surrounding tissue.

Alpha Particle Scattering Experiment

At the beginning of the 20th century, discoveries about the nature of the atom and nuclear processes began to answer the mystery of the source of the Sun's energy.

In 1911, there was a ground-breaking experiment – the **Rutherford–Geiger–Marsden** alpha particle scattering experiment. In this experiment a thin **gold foil** was bombarded with alpha particles. The effect on the **alpha particles** was recorded and these observations provided the evidence for our current understanding of atoms.

Three observations were recorded:

- Most alpha particles were seen to **pass straight through** the gold foil.
- Some particles were **deflected** slightly.
- A few particles **bounced back** towards the source.

Particles passing through the foil indicated that gold atoms are composed of large amounts of space. The deflection and bouncing back of particles indicated that these alpha particles passed close to something positively charged within the atom and were repelled by it.

The deflection of alpha particles is affected by the charge and speed.

Alpha particle

Most particles passed straight through

Some particles were deflected back

Gold atom

Some particles were deflected slightly

Conclusions of the Experiment

The observations of this experiment led Rutherford, Marsden and Geiger to conclude the following:

- Gold atoms, and therefore all atoms, consist largely of empty space with a small, dense core. They called this core the **nucleus**.
- The nucleus is positively charged.
- The **electrons** are arranged around the nucleus with a great deal of space between them.

Quick Test

1. Why can ionising radiation be dangerous?
2. Explain the different risks for the different types of radiation.
3. Explain how high-energy gamma rays can be used in the treatment of cancer. Mention precautions that need to be taken.
4. What was observed in the gold-foil alpha particle scattering experiment?
5. What were the conclusions of the experiment?

Nuclear Fission and Generating Electricity

Nuclear Fission

In a **chemical reaction** it's the electrons that cause the change. The elements involved stay the same but join up in different ways.

Nuclear fission takes place in the nucleus of the atom and different elements are formed:

- A **neutron** is absorbed by a large and unstable **uranium-235** nucleus. This splits the nucleus into two roughly equal-sized, smaller nuclei. This releases energy and more neutrons.
- A fission reaction releases far more energy than even the most **exothermic** chemical reactions.

Once fission has taken place, the neutrons can be absorbed by other nuclei and further fission reactions can take place.

This is a **chain reaction**. A chain reaction occurs when there's enough **fissile material** to prevent too many neutrons escaping without being absorbed. This is called **critical mass** and ensures every reaction triggers at least one further reaction.

Only uranium and plutonium can undergo nuclear fission in this way.

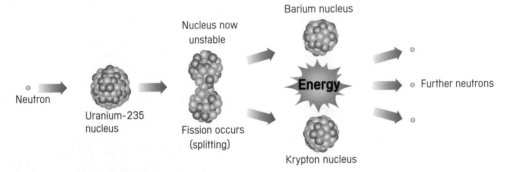

Neutron → Uranium-235 nucleus → Nucleus now unstable / Fission occurs (splitting) → Energy → Barium nucleus / Krypton nucleus / Further neutrons

The Nuclear Reactor

Nuclear power stations use fission reactions to generate the heat needed to produce **steam**. The **nuclear reactor** controls the chain reaction so that the energy is steadily released.

Fission occurs in the **fuel rods** and causes them to become very hot. The **coolant** is a fluid pumped through the reactor. The coolant heats up and is then used in the **heat exchanger** to turn water into steam.

Control rods, made of **boron**, absorb neutrons, preventing the chain reaction getting out of control. Moving the control rods in and out of the **reactor core** changes the amount of fission that takes place.

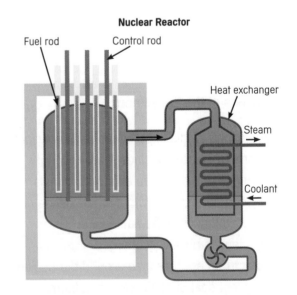

Nuclear Reactor

Fuel rod — Control rod — Heat exchanger — Steam — Coolant

Quick Test

1. Where in the atom does nuclear fission take place?
2. How does the process of fission take place?
3. What is produced in the fission of U-235?

1 **a)** A radioactive isotope has the symbol $^{192}_{77}Ir$.

    i) How many protons are there in a nucleus of this isotope? **[1]**

    ii) How many neutrons does a nucleus of this isotope contain? **[1]**

b) What is an isotope? **[2]**

c) When this isotope decays it emits a beta particle and an isotope of platinum (Pt) is formed. Write down the equation for this decay. **[2]**

d) This isotope is used to treat a tumour which is quite close under the skin. Explain why beta radiation is more suitable than alpha or gamma radiation to treat this tumour. **[3]**

e) The treatment is expected to destroy the tumour in several days.

    i) What would be the most suitable half-life for the source?

       A 60 minutes   **B** 60 hours   **C** 60 days   **D** 60 years **[1]**

    ii) Explain your choice. **[2]**

2 a) What is a chain reaction? **[6]**

....

....

....

....

....

....

b) An isotope of uranium has an atomic number of 92 and a mass number of 238. It decays by emitting an alpha particle. What will be the mass number and the atomic number of the element formed as a result of the decay? **[1]**

....

c) Describe the process of controlled fission of U-235 in a nuclear reactor. **[6]**

....

....

....

....

....

....

3 The explosion at the Chernobyl nuclear reactor released a large cloud of radioactive gas into the atmosphere, which spread over Europe. The gas contained caesium-137 (with a half-life of 30 years) and iodine-131.

The table shows measurements of a count rate from a small sample of iodine-131.

Time (days)	0	4	8	12
Count Rate (Bq)	320	230	160	115

a) Using the data in the table, work out the half-life of iodine-131. **[1]**

....

b) Four months after the explosion, scientists were less concerned about the health risks from the iodine but were still worried about the effects from caesium-137. Do you think they were right to be concerned? Explain your answer. **[3]**

....

....

....

4 In their experiment with gold foil, Rutherford, Geiger and Marsden aimed alpha particles at thin gold foil.

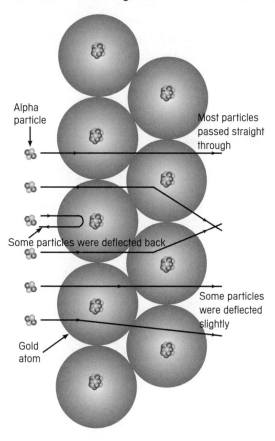

Alpha particle

Most particles passed straight through

Some particles were deflected back

Some particles were deflected slightly

Gold atom

Some of the alpha particles were deflected.

a) Explain why Rutherford, Geiger and Marsden removed air from the apparatus. **[2]**

b) Describe the force that caused some alpha particles to deflect. **[2]**

c) Rutherford, Geiger and Marsden concluded that each gold atom has a small, dense, positively charged nucleus.

Explain how the results of the experiment led to this conclusion. **[5]**

Answers

In the examination, there are three assessment objectives that are tested throughout the exam papers:

AO1 Knowledge and understanding (worth approx. 45–50% of marks in the exam)

AO2 Application of knowledge and understanding, analysis and evaluation (worth approx. 27–33% of marks in the exam)

AO3 Experimental skills, analysis and evaluation of data and methods (worth approx 20–25% of marks in the exam)

Forces and Motion

Answers to Quick Test Questions

Page 5

1. Distance and time
2. Speed
3. You can investigate motion using a trolley, a ramp and ticker tape. The apparatus is shown in the diagram.

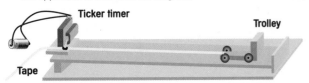

You can take measurements of time (s), distance from start (cm), distance covered in last 0.1s (cm) and therefore average speed for last 0.1s (cm/s). You can use the results to draw a distance–time graph and a velocity–time graph.

Page 7

1. $\text{Acceleration} = \dfrac{\text{Change in velocity}}{\text{Time taken for change}}$
2. It is slowing down; decelerating at a rate of 5m/s^2.
3. Scalar quantities include mass, energy, speed, time; vector quantities include velocity, force, acceleration.

Page 10

1. The overall effect of adding or subtracting more than one force
2. A force that opposes motion
3. 50N
4. 2N
5. The centre of gravity (C of G) of an object is the point through which the whole mass of the object is considered to act. It can be thought of as the point where all the mass is concentrated.
6. The object on the right has its centre of gravity inside its pivot so it is stable. The object on the left has its centre of gravity outside its pivot so it is unstable.

Page 12

1.

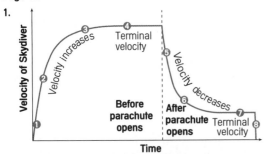

2. **Before the parachute opens:** 1. When the skydiver jumps, he initially accelerates due to the force of gravity; 2. As he falls, he experiences the frictional force of air resistance (R) in the opposite direction. At this point, weight (W) is greater than R, so he continues to accelerate; 3. As his velocity increases, so does the air resistance acting on him; 4. Air resistance increases until it's equal to W. The resultant force now acting on him is zero and his falling velocity becomes constant as forces are balanced. This velocity is called the terminal velocity.

After the parachute opens: 5. When the parachute is opened, unbalanced forces act again because the upward force of R is greatly increased and is bigger than W; 6. The increase in R decreases his velocity. As his velocity decreases, so does R; 7. R decreases until it's equal to W. The forces acting are once again balanced and for the second time, he falls at a steady velocity, although slower than before. This is a new terminal velocity.

3. You can investigate terminal velocity using a tall tube filled with olive oil and a steel ball, as shown in the diagram.

You take measurements of distance fallen through the oil and time taken for each distance. The speed can be calculated. You can measure the mass of the ball and, from the record of time and calculations of speed, calculate the acceleration. Using F = ma you can therefore work out the force on the ball.

4. The thinking distance and the braking distance
5. Vehicle going faster; driver ill, tired, under influence of alcohol or drugs; driver distracted or not concentrating

Page 14

1. Total momentum before collision = Total momentum after
2. Increasing the stopping or collision time; increasing the stopping or collision distance
3. When an object collides with another, or two bodies interact, they exert equal and opposite forces on each other.

Page 16

1. Moment of the force (Nm) = Force in newtons (N) x Perpendicular distance from the line of action of the force to the pivot in metres (m)
2. Total clockwise moment = Total anticlockwise moment
3. It recovers its original shape.
4. For elastic objects, the extension is directly proportional to the force applied, provided that the limit of proportionality is not exceeded.

Page 18

1. The Universe is approximately 14 000 million years old – much older than the Sun.
2. A galaxy is a collection of billions of stars.
3. The Milky Way
4. 169N
5. Comets have elliptical orbits; planets have near circular orbits.
6. 1754km/h to the nearest km/h

Answers

Answers to Exam Practice Questions

AO1 **1. a)** A3; B2; C1 **[2 marks for all correct, 1 mark for 1 correct]**
AO1   **b)** The speed **[1 mark]**
AO1 **2. a)** 8m/s **should be ringed.** **[1 mark]**
AO1   **b)** 7.5m/s² **should be ringed.** **[1 mark]**
AO1 **3.** Velocity–time graphs are used in lorry tachographs to make sure drivers rest for the appropriate time **should be ticked** **[1 mark]**
    Friction is a force that always opposes motion **should be ticked** **[1 mark]**
AO3 **4.** Without friction it would be impossible to walk **[1 mark]**. There is a frictional force that is experienced by the shoe and acts in the direction the person is walking in **[1 mark]**. The force experienced by the pavement is in the opposite direction and has the same magnitude **[1 mark]**. As the person wearing the shoe has a much smaller mass than the ground, the person moves forward relative to the ground **[1 mark]**.

A question worth 4 marks needs to contain 4 clear points.

AO1 **5. a)** Momentum = 1500 × 45 **[1 mark]** = 67 500kg m/s **[1 mark]**

In calculation questions, a mark will normally be given for the correct calculation, even if the answer is then incorrect. So, it's very important to show all your workings.

AO1   **b)** Acceleration = $\frac{55-45}{4}$ **[1 mark]** = 2.5m/s² **[1 mark]**
AO1 **6.** The change in momentum depends on the size of the force acting and the time it acts for **should be ticked [1 mark]**
    If the resultant force on a car is zero, its momentum is constant **should be ticked. [1 mark]**
AO1 **7. a)** Change in momentum = 150 × 3 − (150 × −2) **[1 mark]**
    (Remember the velocity of rebound will be negative.)
    Change in momentum = 450 + 300 = 750kg m/s **[1 mark]**

AO1   **b)** Force × 0.5 = 750 **[1 mark]** , so force = 1500N **[1 mark]**
AO2   **c)** To increase **[1 mark]** the impact time **[1 mark]**, which reduces the force on his body **[1 mark]**
AO1 **8. a)** Change in velocity **[1 mark]** and time taken **[1 mark]**
AO1   **b)** Straight line with a positive gradient − Acceleration
    Straight line with a negative gradient − Deceleration
    Horizontal straight line − Constant velocity **[2 marks for all correct; 1 mark if only 1 or 2 correct]**
AO2 **9. a)** C **[1 mark]**
AO2   **b)** 32m **[accept 30–34m] [1 mark]**
AO2   **c)** Thinking distance is increased if: the vehicle is travelling faster, if the driver is ill, if the driver is tired or if the driver is under the influence of alcohol or drugs. **[Accept any 2 for 2 marks]**
AO1 **10.** Air bags; Crumple zones; Seatbelts; Safety cages **[any three for 3 marks]**
AO1 **11. a)** Air resistance/drag **[1 mark]**
AO1   **b)** X becomes larger. **[1 mark]**
AO1   **c)** Terminal velocity **[1 mark]**
AO1   **d)** 600N **[1 mark]**
AO1 **12.** 1100 × $\frac{22.3-13.4}{20}$ **[1 mark]** = 489.5N **[1 mark]**
AO1 **13. a)** 30 000N **[1 mark]**
AO2   **b)** 30 000 = x × 2 where x is mass of concrete block **[1 mark]**
    x = 15 000kg **[1 mark]**
AO1 **14. a)** A comet has an elliptical orbit **[1 mark]**; a planet has a near oval orbit. **[1 mark]**
AO1   **b)** $\frac{1.43 \times 10^{12}}{5.9 \times 10^{7}}$ **[1 mark]** = 2.4 × 10⁴ m/s **[1 mark]**
    = 24 000 m/s (to 2 sf) **[1 mark]**
AO1   **c)** The Universe has billions of galaxies **[1 mark]**; a galaxy has billions of stars. **[1 mark]**

Electricity

Answers to Quick Test Questions

Page 25
1.

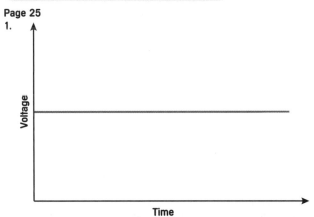

Time / Voltage

2. It connects the holder to the mains supply, which is likely to be lethal.
3. An RCCB operates by detecting a difference in the current between the live and neutral wires.
4. The case will become live; the current will then 'flow to earth' through the earth wire as this offers least resistance; this overload of current will cause the fuse to melt (or circuit breaker to trip), breaking the circuit. The appliance (and user) is therefore protected.

Page 27
1. 13A

2. The total current through the whole circuit is the sum of the currents through the separate components: I = I₁ + I₂.
3. Each branch can be operated independently of the others. So a lamp (light) in one branch can be switched off without affecting the lights (lamps) in the other branches.

Page 29
1. Its resistance decreases.
2. R = $\frac{V}{I}$
3. 15Ω   4. 0.3A
5. $\frac{690}{240}$ = 2.875C = 2.9C (to 2 sf)

Page 31
1. In a metal structure, the atoms exist as ions surrounded by an electron cloud. If a potential difference is applied to the metal, the electrons in this cloud are able to move, creating the flow of a current, i.e. a current.
2. Teflon®
3. You could charge up a Perspex rod by rubbing it with a cloth.
4. They will repel each other.
5. Negatively charged

Page 33
1. The danger of electrostatics can be reduced by making sure appliances are correctly earthed, using insulation mats effectively and wearing shoes with insulating soles.

Answers

2. A discharge of static electricity (i.e. a spark) can lead to an explosion.

3. The paint particles are given a negative charge so that they repel each other, forming a fine spray. This ensures that the paint is applied evenly. The panel to be sprayed is positively charged, so it attracts the negatively charged paint.

Answers to Exam Practice Questions

AO1 **1. a)** False – electrons have negative charge. **[1 mark]**

AO1   **b)** **Any two from:** Spray painting; Smoke precipitators; Defibrillators **[Any two for 2 marks]**

AO1 **2. a)** Neutral – blue, earth – green and yellow, live – brown **[All correct for 2 marks]**

AO1   **b)** False – they still require a fuse. **[1 mark]**

AO1 **3. a)** $\frac{12V}{0.3A}$ **[1 mark]** = 40Ω **[1 mark]**

AO1   **b)** $\frac{12V}{80Ω}$ **[1 mark]** = 0.15A **[1 mark]**

AO1 **4.** The two rods will attract each other. **[1 mark]**

AO1 **5.**

Component	Voltage (V)	Current (A)	Resistance (Ω)
Lamp	8	**2**	4
Resistor	**30**	6	5
Coil	24	4	**6**

[3 marks]

AO3 **6. a) (i)** Thermistor **[1 mark]**
       (ii) They're inversely proportional **[accept 'there is negative correlation']. [1 mark]**

AO3   **b) Any one from:** Read ammeter incorrectly; Not put thermistor in ice; Not measured temperature correctly **[1 mark]**

Review your practical notes to see where errors may occur.

AO1 **7. a)** When an electrical charge (current) flows through a resistor (e.g. electrical device or appliance), the resistor gets hot. **[1 mark]** Some of the electrical energy is used but a lot of energy is wasted, which usually heats the surroundings. **[1 mark]**

AO1   **b) i)** P = I x V **[1 mark]**

AO1   **ii)** $\frac{1100}{110}$ **[1 mark]** = 10A **[1 mark]**

AO1   **c)** If there is a sudden surge in current the wire in the fuse will heat up and melt **[1 mark]**, which breaks the circuit **[1 mark]** and stops any further current flowing. **[1 mark]**

AO1   **d)** Direct current: voltage stays constant with time **[1 mark]**; alternating current: voltage varies with time **[1 mark]**

AO3 **8. a)** Suspend two insulating rods near to each other **[1 mark]** on insulated thin wire. Rub both rods with a cloth **[1 mark]** If they are the same charge they will repel **[1 mark]**; if they are different charges they will attract. **[1 mark]**

AO1   **b)** The electrons in a metal can flow easily **[1 mark]**, so if electrons were transferred onto the surface they would flow away rather than staying on the surface and allowing the material to become charged **[1 mark]**

AO1 **9. a)** Positive **[1 mark]**, in order to attract the negatively charged paint droplets **[1 mark]**

AO1   **b)** The paint drops are charged so repel each other **[1 mark]**, so the spray is finer than it would otherwise have been and the paint will spread out evenly **[1 mark]**. The paint is attracted to the car **[1 mark]** and so it is less likely to be wasted by falling to the floor. It will also be attracted to curved areas. **[1 mark]**

Waves

Answers to Quick Test Questions

Page 40

1. Frequency is the number of waves produced (or that pass a particular point) in 1 second.
2. Longitudinal: each particle moves backwards and forwards about its normal position in the same plane as the direction of wave movement; Transverse: each particle moves up and down about its normal position at 90° to the direction of wave movement.
3. Energy – they do not carry matter.
4. The amplitude is the maximum disturbance caused by a wave.
5. Longitudinal
6. 0.5m/s
7. Frequency
8. 10m
9. When the gap is the same width as the wavelength of the wave passing through it.

Page 42

1. 3×10^8m/s
2. **Examples:** Radio waves – television and radio signals; Microwaves – mobile phone networks and satellite communication, cooking; Infrared – remote controls for TVs, grills, optical fibre communication; Visible light – morse code with torches, photography, fibre optics; Ultraviolet – fluorescent lamps; X-rays – observing the internal structure of objects and materials, medical applications; Gamma rays – sterilising food and medical equipment
3. They are very reactive.
4. **Any two from:** The heating effect (sunburn); Ionising radiation can age the skin; It can cause mutations; It can lead to radiation poisoning

5. Microwave ovens have a metal case and a wire screen in the door to absorb microwaves and stop too much radiation escaping.

Page 45

1. Refractive index = $\frac{\sin i}{\sin r}$

2.

Light Reflected by a Plane Mirror

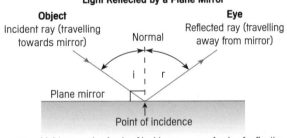

    → = Light ray   i = Angle of incidence   r = Angle of reflection

3. The critical angle is the maximum angle of incidence (measured from the normal) before total internal reflection occurs.
4. Total internal reflection only occurs when light travels from a medium with a high refractive index into a medium with a lower refractive index and the angle of incidence is more than the critical angle.
5. The higher a medium's refractive index, the lower its critical angle or $\sin c = \frac{1}{n}$.

Page 47

1. An analogue signal can have almost any value and can vary with time.
2. A digital signal is made up from a string of bits using just two values, 0 and 1.

3. Digital signals can travel long distances at a higher quality than analogue signals. This is because analogue signals can have many different values, so it's hard to distinguish between noise and the original signal; this means that noise can't be completely removed. Digital signals only have two states, on (1) or off (0), so they can still be recognised despite any noise that's picked up; this means that any interference can be removed.

4. When digital signals carry noise, it's clear which parts of the signal represent 1 and 0, so the signal can be regenerated without the noise.

Page 49

1. 20Hz–20 000Hz
2. Ultrasound scanning and imaging.
3. About 1m
4. Place a sound source and two microphones in a straight line, with the sound source at one end. Measure the distance between the microphones (x), called microphone basis. Measure the time of arrival between the signals (delay) reaching the different microphones (t). The speed of sound $= \frac{x}{t}$

Answers to Exam Practice Questions

AO1 1. a) It is being refracted. **[1 mark]**

AO1   b) Waves travel from one medium to another. **[1 mark]** This causes wave speed to change **[1 mark]** and the wave to change direction. **[1 mark]**

AO1 2. 36m/s **[1 mark]**

AO1 3. Amplitude – a measurement of how much energy a wave carries; Frequency – the number of waves made per second by a source; Wavelength – the distance between the corresponding points on two adjacent cycles **[1 mark for two correct answers; 2 marks for all three correct answers]**

AO1 4. $\frac{3 \times 10^8}{9 \times 10^8}$ **[1 mark]** = 0.33m **[1 mark]**

AO1 5. a) A2; B3; C1 **[3 marks]**

AO1   b)

[3 marks]

AO1   c) $\frac{330}{2000}$ **[1 mark]** = 0.165m **[1 mark]**

AO2   d) Sound waves need a medium to travel in **[1 mark]**; water molecules are closer together than air molecules **[1 mark]**; sound waves are therefore transmitted through the material at a faster rate. **[1 mark]**

AO1 6. a) The speed of light increases as light travels from Perspex to the air **[1 mark]** so the ray is refracted.

AO1   b) Critical angle **[1 mark]**

AO2   c) An endoscope is a flexible tube that can be used for seeing inside objects and into places that would otherwise be inaccessible **[1 mark]**. An example of its use is when it is used by doctors to look inside a patient's body **[1 mark]**. An endoscope has two bundles of optical fibres **[1 mark]**; one set is used for transmitting light from a source to light up the object **[1 mark]**, the other set carries the light rays reflected by the object back to form an image **[1 mark]**. The light travels along the fibres and total internal reflection keeps the light rays inside the fibres. **[1 mark]**

AO1 7. A digital signal only has two values, 0 and 1 **[1 mark]**, but an analogue signal varies in value continuously **[1 mark]**.

AO1 8. a) Ultraviolet; Visible light; Infrared; Radio waves **[2 marks]**

AO2   b) The hills have gaps roughly the size of the wavelength of the radio waves, so the radio waves are diffracted **[1 mark]** and spread out around the hills. The microwaves for the mobile phone signals have smaller wavelength and are not diffracted **[1 mark]**, so the straight beams of microwave radiation are blocked by the hills. **[1 mark]**

AO3 9. a) The simplest method to measure the speed of sound in air uses two microphones **[1 mark]** and a fast recording device such as a digital storage scope **[1 mark]**. Place a sound source and two microphones in a straight line, with the sound source at one end **[1 mark]**. Measure the distance between the microphones (x), called microphone basis **[1 mark]**. Measure the time of arrival between the signals (delay) **[1 mark]** reaching the different microphones (t). The speed of sound $= \frac{x}{t}$ **[1 mark]**

AO3   b) The voltage–time graph gives the time taken for one cycle of the wave (which is the period) **[1 mark]**. Since $T = \frac{1}{f}$ **[1 mark]** you can work out the frequency **[1 mark]**.

You should quote formulae where relevant in your answers.

Energy Resources and Energy Transfer

Answers to Quick Test Questions

Page 55

1. Energy cannot be created or destroyed, only transferred from one form to another.
2. **Any three from:** Thermal; Light; Electrical; Sound; Kinetic; Chemical; Nuclear; Potential (elastic and gravitational)
3. It is wasted, turns into heat and warms the surroundings.
4. 12.5%
5. It is an energy transfer diagram using arrows that are proportional to the amount of energy involved in each process.

Page 57

1. As a metal becomes hotter the atoms vibrate more vigorously. This additional energy is transferred to the cooler parts of the metal by the free electrons that roam throughout the metal.
2. Particles in the liquid or gas nearest the energy source move faster, causing the substance to expand and become less dense. The warm liquid or gas now rises vertically. As it does so it cools, becomes denser and eventually sinks. The colder, denser liquid or gas moves into the space created (close to the heat source) and the cycle repeats.

3. A dark, matt surface, because it is a better emitter of heat at a given temperature.
4. Conduction and convection; by trapping layers of air, a good insulator, between the fibres

Page 60

1. 200W
2. 4.32 x 10^6J
3. It increases four-fold
4. Joules (J)
5. Work done by motor is transferred into GPE for the skier.

Page 62

1. **Any five from:** Coal; Gas; Oil; Nuclear; Wind; Water (hydroelectric, tidal, wave); Solar; Biofuel
2. Global warming; Climate change
3. Advantage – relatively cheap and easy to extract. Disadvantage – **any one from:** burning produces carbon dioxide (greenhouse gas) and sulfur dioxide (acid rain) emissions into atmosphere; perhaps only several hundred years of coal supplies left.
4. Advantage – **any one from:** relatively easy to find; perhaps large amounts of reserve stocks available; doesn't produce sulfur dioxide emissions into the atmosphere. Disadvantage – **any one from:**

Answers

burning produces carbon dioxide (though less than coal or oil) and some sulfur dioxide; expensive pipelines and networks are required; visual pollution of landscape; destruction of wildlife habitats.

Page 63
1. A fuel that can be obtained from biological material. It can be a solid, liquid or gas.
2. Advantage – **any one from:** uses light from the Sun; useful in remote locations; no polluting gases emitted; small-scale production possible. Disadvantage – **any one from:** depends on light intensity; use of high cost semiconductor materials; efficiency is poor; visual pollution of large areas of solar panels.

Answers to Exam Practice Questions

AO1   1. $1200 \times 15 \times 60$ **[1 mark]** $= 1.08 \times 10^6$ J **[1 mark]**

AO1   2. PE = mgh

$h = \dfrac{30}{0.16 \times 10}$ **[1 mark]** $= 18.75$ m **[1 mark]**

AO2   3. mgh $= \dfrac{1}{2}$ mv², so 2gh $= v^2$. $2 \times 10 \times 30 = v^2$, $v = \sqrt{600}$

[2 marks] $= 24.5$ m/s **[1 mark]**

AO1   4. It is generated from another energy source such as fossil fuels or nuclear power **[1 mark]**.

AO1   5. To show the input and output energy in a system **[1 mark]** and thus the efficiency of energy transfers **[1 mark]**

AO1   6. Kinetic to electrical **[1 mark]**

AO1   7.

Electrical appliance	Energy in	Useful energy out	Efficiency
Iron	2000J/s	Heat: 1600J/s	**80%**
Radio	200J/s	Sound: 60J/s	**30%**
Computer	400J/s	Light: 180J/s Sound: 80J/s	**65%**

[3 marks]

AO1   8. 37% **[1 mark]**
AO2   9. a) Carpet is an insulator and so heat from the feet does not get conducted away from them by the carpet **[1 mark]**, whereas stone would conduct some of the heat away and feet would feel colder. **[1 mark]**
AO2   b) Layer of air between the blankets **[1 mark]** stops heat escaping **[1 mark]**
AO2   c) Smoke is carried upwards by convection currents **[1 mark]**, so there is less smoke at floor level. **[1 mark]**
AO2   d) Cold water is heated by an element at the bottom of the kettle **[1 mark]** and then rises by convection currents. **[1 mark]**
AO2   e) Black surfaces radiate more heat **[1 mark]** and cool quicker. **[1 mark]**
AO1   10. a) $\dfrac{8}{100} \times 100$ **[1 mark]** $= 8\%$ **[1 mark]**
AO1   b) It is transferred to heat. **[1 mark]**
AO1   c) $0.4x = 8W$

$x = \dfrac{8}{0.4}$ **[1 mark]** $= 20W$ **[1 mark]**

AO2   11. a) Gravitational **[1 mark]**
AO2   b) Elastic potential **[1 mark]**
AO2   c) Kinetic **[1 mark]**
AO2   d) Reduction of height of bounce **[1 mark]**
AO2   e) Gets very slightly warmer **[1 mark]**; energy transferred away as heat **[1 mark]**
AO1   12. a) GPE = mgh **[1 mark]**
AO1   b) $9 \times 10 \times 8$ **[1 mark]** $= 720$ J **[1 mark]**

Solids, Liquids and Gases

Answers to Quick Test Questions

Page 69
1. Density $= \dfrac{\text{Mass}}{\text{Volume}}$
2. 2g/cm³
3. Mass = Density × Volume = $7.8 \times 15 = 117$ g
4. 20Pa
5. Particles in a fluid or a gas are constantly moving. They constantly collide with each other and the walls of the container. These collisions cause a force on the other particles and the walls of the container. This force is usually described in terms of the pressure it causes in a particular area.
6. 7500Pa

Page 70

1.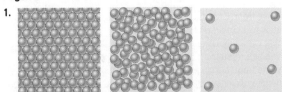

2. Particles break away from the surface of a liquid to form a vapour. The more energetic particles break away from the surface. This reduces the average energy of the molecules remaining in the liquid and so the liquid cools.

Page 73
1. When the molecules hit the walls of a container, they exert a force on it. It is this force, divided by the surface area of the container, that is observed when measuring pressure.
2. Small particles, such as pollen or fine smoke particles, can be seen through a microscope moving in a random way. The reason for this is that the particles are constantly being hit by even smaller particles, which are too small to see (e.g. water or air molecules).
3. If you keep cooling a material down, absolute zero is the temperature at which all movement of the molecules has stopped.
4. 273K
5. 338K
6. Higher temperature means higher average speed of molecules
7. Pressure increases.
8. The pressure is halved.
9. 2900cm³

Answers to Exam Practice Questions

AO3   1. a) i) 219g **[1 mark for calculation; 1 for correct answer]**
AO3   ii) 172cm³ **[1 mark]**
AO3   b) 1.27g/cm³ **[1 mark for calculation; 1 for correct answer]**

AO1 **2. a)**

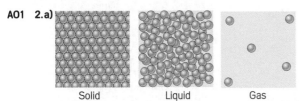

Solid   Liquid   Gas

[3 marks]

Make sure diagrams are clear and labelled.

AO1 **b)** They 'slide' over each other in a random motion. **[1 mark]**

AO1 **c)** Evaporation; boiling **[1 mark]**

AO2 **3.** Pressure is greater at bottom of full cup **[1 mark]**; pressure = height × density × g **[1 mark]**; density, area and g same in both cups **[1 mark]**; height greater in full cup, so pressure greater **[1 mark]**

AO1 **4. a) i)** Pressure difference = Density of water × Depth × Gravitational field strength **[1 mark]**

Make sure you learn all necessary equations.

AO1 **ii)** 1 230 000Pa **[3 marks]**

AO1 **iii)** All directions **[1 mark]**

AO1 **b)** The weight of the gases in the air acts over the area of the human body **[1 mark]**; $\frac{\text{Force}}{\text{Area}}$ = Pressure **[1 mark]**

AO1 **5. a) i)** 373K **[1 mark]**

AO1 **ii)** **Any one from:** Molecules in water have less kinetic energy; Molecules in water move less quickly; Molecules in water move more slowly **[1 mark]**

AO2 **b)** Molecules are in motion **[1 mark]**; collide with and bounce off sides of kettle **[1 mark]**; momentum changes as they do **[1 mark]**, so force is produced with change of momentum; Pressure = $\frac{\text{Force}}{\text{Area}}$ **[1 mark]**

AO1 **c)** $\frac{120 \times 850}{101}$ **[1 mark]** = 1010cm³ **[1 mark]**

Remember to show the units.

AO1 **d)** Pressure decreases. Molecules lower in temperature so have lower kinetic energy; molecules hit sides of the cylinder less frequently so less change in momentum, so lower force.

Same area, lower force: Pressure = $\frac{\text{Force}}{\text{Area}}$, so pressure lower. **[2 marks]**

Magnetism and Electromagnetism

Answers to Quick Test Questions

Page 79
1. They repel each other.
2. It stays magnetic once it has been magnetised.
3. Two magnets will attract in one orientation and repel in the other – a magnet will attract a soft magnetic material whichever end of the material is facing the magnet.
4. A region of space around magnets where their magnetism affects other objects
5. A line that shows the path that a free north pole would take from a north pole to a south pole

Page 81
1. Straight lines through the centre of the coil
2. It experiences a force.
3. Reverse direction of current; reverse direction of magnetic field
4. No, only when an electric current flows through electromagnet
5.

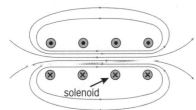

solenoid

Page 83
1. A simple d.c. motor works by using a current-carrying coil. The current flowing through the coil creates a magnetic field. The magnetic field of the magnet and the magnetic field of the coil interact. Each side of the coil experiences a force in an opposite direction because the current is flowing in opposite directions in the two parts of the coil. The forces combine to make the coil rotate.
2. The coil is attached to a paper cone. The changing current in the coil produces a changing magnetic field which interacts with the field from the permanent magnet. This creates a backwards and forwards motion of the coil and paper cone. This makes the air vibrate – a sound wave.
3. Decrease size of current; decrease strength of magnetic field

Page 84
1. The magnetic field is being cut.
2. There is no induced current.

3. By increasing the speed of rotation of the magnet; increasing the strength of the magnetic field, possibly by using an electromagnet; increasing the number of turns on the coil; placing an iron core inside the coil

Page 86
1. Soft iron core and two coils (primary and secondary)
2. Alternating current
3. 5.75A
4. 4000 turns

Answers to Exam Practice Questions

AO1 **1. a)** Arrows drawn so side X moves up **[1 mark]** and side Y moves down **[1 mark]**

AO1 **b)** Fleming's left-hand rule **[1 mark]**

AO1 **c)** Coil of wire is on spindle, and forces produce a moment or turning force **[1 mark]**; this makes coil rotate about axle **[1 mark]**

AO1 **d)** Motor effect **[1 mark]**

AO1 **e)** Direction of motion would be reversed **[1 mark]**

AO1 **f)** **Any two from:** Increase size of current; Increase strength of magnetic field; More turns on coil **[2 marks]**

AO1 **2.** **Any two from:** Spin magnet faster; Increase number of turns on coil; Use stronger magnet; Place an iron core inside the coil **[2 marks]**

AO1 **3. a)** Jake **[1 mark]**

AO1 **b)** Jessie and Sonny **[both needed for mark]**

AO1 **4.** An alternating potential difference across the primary coil **[1 mark]** produces an alternating magnetic field in the iron core **[1 mark]**. This alternating field passes backwards and forwards around the iron core and through the secondary coil **[1 mark]**, which has more turns than the primary coil **[1 mark]**. This induces an alternating potential difference across the secondary coil **[1 mark]** which will be higher than the input alternating voltage **[1 mark]**.

AO2 **5.** 18 000 **[1 mark]**

AO3 **6. a)** **Any two from:** Current flows in coil; Produces magnetic field; Resultant force on coil/interaction of magnetic fields **[2 marks]**

AO3 **b)** **Any two from:** Decrease current; Weaker magnet; Decrease number of turns on coil of motor **[2 marks]**

Answers

AO3 **c)** Coil/wire cuts magnetic field; there is an induced voltage/ current; current in the lamp completes the circuit **[2 marks]**

AO3 **7. a)** Place compass in field and observe needle; make mark to show direction of needle; repeat and join marks to make one field line; repeat on other side of magnet **[3 marks]**

AO1 **b)**

[1 mark for shape, 1 mark for arrow direction]

Ensure that any diagrams are clear.

Radioactivity and Particles

Answers to Quick Test Questions

Page 90
1. Extremely tiny central nucleus composed of protons (positive charge) and neutrons (no electrical charge) surrounded by electrons (negative charge)
2. Number of protons in an atom
3. Number of protons and neutrons in an atom

Page 92
1. Alpha; beta; gamma
2. Alpha
3. Mass number decreases by 4; proton number decreases by 2

Page 93
1. Photographic plate or Geiger–Muller tube
2. **Answers may include:** Medical; Radon gas; Gamma rays; Food; Cosmic rays; Nuclear industry

Page 95
1. It decreases; the number of particles left to decay decreases with time.
2. A measurement of the time it takes for the rate of decay (count rate) to halve or the time required for half of the original population of radioactive atoms to decay
3. No
4. 8 minutes
5. 24 hours or 1 day

Page 97
1. Ionising radiation can break molecules into ions – these ions can damage living cells and the cells may be killed or become cancerous.
2. Alpha is the most dangerous if the source is inside the body; all the radiation will be absorbed by cells in the body. Beta is the most dangerous if the source is outside the body; unlike alpha, it can penetrate the outer layer of skin and damage internal organs. Gamma can cause harm if it's absorbed by the cells, but it is weakly ionising and can pass straight through the body causing no damage at all.
3. High-energy gamma rays can destroy cancer cells but can damage healthy cells too. The radiation has to be carefully targeted from different angles to minimise the damage.
4. Most alpha particles were seen to pass straight through the gold foil. Some particles were deflected slightly. A few particles bounced back towards the source.
5. Gold atoms, and therefore all atoms, consist largely of empty space with a small, dense core (the nucleus). The nucleus is positively charged. The electrons are arranged around the nucleus with a great deal of space between them.

Page 98
1. In the nucleus
2. A neutron collides with a U−235 nucleus making it more unstable. The splitting of the nucleus releases energy in the form of kinetic energy of fission products
3. Two daughter nuclei and a small number of neutrons

Answers to Exam Practice Questions

AO1 **1. a) i)** 77 **[1 mark]**
AO1 **ii)** 115 **[1 mark]**

AO1 **b)** Atoms of the same element **[1 mark]** with different numbers of neutrons **[1 mark]**

AO1 **c)** $^{192}_{77}Ir \longrightarrow ^{192}_{78}Pt + ^{0}_{-1}\beta$ **[2 marks; 1 mark for symbols, 1 mark for balancing equation]**

Check that equations balance – top and bottom.

AO2 **d)** Alpha radiation is not penetrating enough, it is absorbed before reaching tumour **[1 mark]**; gamma radiation is too penetrating and goes straight through tumour **[1 mark]**; beta penetrates tumour but doesn't go any further than tumour. **[1 mark]**

Remember the properties of ionising radiations.

AO1 **e) i)** 60 hours **[1 mark]**
ii) Activity decreases with time **[1 mark]**; **B** remains sufficiently active for period of treatment; **A** is not effective over period of treatment; and **C** and **D** continue to be active after treatment has finished. **[1 mark]**

AO1 **2. a)** A chain reaction is when a uranium (or plutonium) nucleus absorbs a neutron, becoming unstable **[1 mark]**. It then splits into two smaller nuclei, **[1 mark]** releasing energy and producing three more neutrons **[1 mark]**. There is enough fissile material to prevent too many neutrons **[1 mark]** escaping without being absorbed **[1 mark]**. This is the critical mass and ensures every reaction triggers at least one further reaction **[1 mark]**.

AO1 **b)** Mass number 234; Atomic number 90 **[1 mark]**

AO1 **c)** Neutrons are captured/absorbed; nucleus breaks to form daughter nuclei; and releases energy and releases neutron; spare neutrons lead to chain reaction; moderator slows neutrons down; control rods absorb neutrons and control rate of reaction; energy released used to heat water and turn into steam **[6 marks]**

AO2 **3. a)** 8 days **[1 mark]**

AO2 **b)** Yes. Caesium-137 has a half-life of 30 years **[1 mark]**, so after only four months it is still extremely radioactive **[1 mark]** and poses a severe health hazard. The iodine has an 8-day half life so in 4 months will have almost completely decayed **[1 mark]**

AO1 **4. a)** To avoid / reduce absorption / loss of energy of alpha particles **[1 mark]**; to avoid / reduce changes of alpha particles colliding with air particles (alpha particles absorbed by few cm of air) **[1 mark]**

AO1 **b)** These alpha particles passed close to something positively charged within the atom **[1 mark]** and were repelled by it. **[1 mark]**

AO1 **c)** Undeflected particles showed that most of an atom consists of empty space **[1 mark]**; deflections showed repulsive force which, if electrostatic, must suggest positive charge in centre of atom **[1 mark]**; as only some deflected, nucleus at centre is small **[1 mark]**; as a few bounced back, mass of the nucleus must be greater than that of the alpha particle; **[1 mark]** high density related to high mass and small size. **[1 mark]**

Absolute zero – the lowest possible temperature when the kinetic energy of the molecules is zero.

Acceleration – the rate at which an object changes its velocity.

Activity – the number of ionising particles a radioactive source emits each second.

Air resistance – the frictional force that acts on a moving object.

Alternating current – an electric current that changes direction of flow repeatedly.

Alpha particle – a helium nucleus, 2 protons and 2 neutrons.

Amplitude – the maximum disturbance of a wave from a central position.

Angle of incidence – the angle between a ray falling on a plane surface and the normal line at that point.

Angle of reflection – the angle between the reflected ray leaving a plane surface and the normal line at that point.

Atom – the smallest part of an element; the building blocks of matter.

Atomic number – the number of protons in an atom.

Background radiation – radiation that is around us; predominantly from natural sources.

Beta particle – type of nuclear radiation emitted as an electron by a radioactive nucleus.

Biofuels – a fuel obtained from lifeless or living biological matter.

Braking distance – the distance a car travels during braking to a stop.

Brownian motion – the random motion of particles on a liquid or in a gas.

Centre of gravity – the point in a body from which the force due to gravity appears to be acting on the body.

Circuit – a complete loop around which electricity can flow.

Circuit breaker – electrical switch which protects a circuit from damage.

Chain reaction – a series of nuclear fission reactions where neutrons released from one reaction cause another nuclear fission reaction, and so on.

Conduction – transfer of thermal or electrical energy.

Conductor – material that transfers thermal or electrical energy.

Convection – transfer of heat energy without the movement of the substance.

Critical angle – the largest incident angle at which refraction can occur.

Current – the rate of flow of an electrical charge; measure in amperes (A).

Current–potential difference graph – graph used to show how the current through a component varies with the potential difference across it.

Density – the mass in kilograms of one metre cube of a substance; mass divided by volume.

Diode – an electrical device that allows electric current to flow in one direction only.

Direct current – an electrical current that only flows in one direction.

Distance-time graph – a graph showing distance travelled against time taken; the gradient of the line represents speed.

Double insulated – electrical appliances that need no earth connection.

Earthed – connecting the metal case of an electrical appliance to the earth wire of a plug.

Efficiency – useful output energy expressed as a percentage of total input energy.

Elastic – a force applied to an object that recovers its original shape when the force is removed.

Elastic potential energy – the energy stored in a stretched spring.

Electron – a negatively charged particle that orbits the nucleus of an atom.

Energy – ability to do work; measured in joules (J).

Fleming's left-hand rule – predicts direction of force on a current-carrying wire.

Force – a push or pull acting on an object; measured in newtons (N).

Frequency – the number of waves produced (or that pass a particular point) in one second.

Friction – the resistive force between two surfaces as they move over each other.

Fuse – a thin piece of metal, which overheats and melts to break an electric circuit if it's overloaded.

Gamma radiation – ionising electromagnetic radiation; radioactive and dangerous to health.

Generator – a device in which a magnet spins inside a coil of wire to produce a voltage or an electric current.

Gravitational field strength – the force of gravity on a mass of one kilogram; the unit is the newton per kilogram, and it is different on different planets.

Gravitational potential energy (GPE) – the energy an object has because of its mass and height above the Earth.

Gravity – a force of attraction between masses; the force that keeps objects orbiting larger objects.

Half-life – the time taken for half the atoms in a radioactive material to decay.

Insulator – a substance that doesn't transfer thermal or electrical energy.

Ion – a charged particle formed when an atom gains or loses an electron.

Ionising power – the ability of particles or electromagnetic radiation to ionise other atoms or molecules.

Isotopes – atoms of the same element that contain a different number of neutrons, but the same number of protons.

Joule (J) – unit of energy.

Kelvin scale of temperature – a scale of temperature that starts at absolute zero.

Glossary

Kinetic energy – energy a body has because of its movement.

Kinetic theory – theory describing movement of molecules in gases, liquids and solids.

Law of conservation of energy – energy cannot be created or destroyed.

Magnetic field – the area of effect of a magnet (or the Earth) indicated by lines of force surrounding the magnet (or the Earth).

Mains electricity – electricity supplied centrally to households and businesses.

Mass – the quantity of matter in an object.

Mass number – the number of protons and neutrons in an atomic nucleus.

Neutron – a subatomic particle found in the nucleus; has no charge.

Non-renewable energy source – an energy source that can't be replaced as fast as it is used.

Nuclear fission – the splitting of atomic nuclei.

Nuclear fusion – process whereby nuclei of small atoms join to make a larger nucleus, releasing energy.

Period (of wave) – inverse of frequency.

Potential difference (voltage) – the difference in potential between two points in an electrical circuit; the energy transferred in a circuit by each coulomb of charge; measured in volts (V).

Power – the rate of doing work; measured in watts (W).

Pressure – the effect of force spread out over an area;
pressure is equal to $\dfrac{\text{force}}{\text{area}}$;
pressure difference in a fluid = density × g × height difference.

Primary energy source – energy source directly from Earth, e.g. coal.

Proton – a subatomic particle found in the nucleus; has a charge of +1.

Radioactive – substance that emits radiation from its atomic nuclei.

Reflection – change in direction of a wave at a boundary between two media.

Refraction – change in direction of a light ray as it passes from one medium to another and changes speed.

Refractive index – a measure of a medium's ability to bend light due to slowing the light down.

Renewable – energy sources that will not run out.

Residual Current Circuit Breaker (RCCB) – automatic device for breaking a circuit; based on detecting a difference in current between the live and neutral wires.

Resistor – an electrical device that resists the flow of an electric current.

Resistance – how hard it is to get a current through a component at a particular potential difference; measured in ohms (Ω).

Risk – the danger (normally to health) associated with a procedure, action or event.

Sankey diagram – an energy transfer diagram where the widths of the arrows are proportional to the amount of energy used.

Speed – the rate at which an object moves.

Terminal velocity – maximum velocity of a falling object.

Thermistor – a resistor whose resistance varies with temperature.

Thinking distance – the distance that a car travels whilst the driver reacts and starts to brake.

Total internal reflection – complete reflection of a light or infrared ray back into a medium.

Transfer – moving energy from one place to another.

Transformer – an electrical device that changes the voltage of electrical circuits.

Unstable nuclei – nuclei that can decay.

Velocity–time graph – a graph showing velocity against time.

Voltage (potential difference) – the difference in potential between two points in an electrical circuit; the energy transferred in a circuit by each coulomb of charge; measured in volts (V).

Wavelength – the distance between corresponding points on two adjacent disturbances.

P2 **Analogue** – signal varies continuously in amplitude/ frequency.

Conservation of momentum – the total momentum before and after a collision is the same.

Diffraction – the spreading out of a wave as a result of passing an obstacle through a gap.

Digital – signal that uses only 0s and 1s.

Earthing – connecting appliance to earth using earth wire.

Gas – state of matter where particles are very spread out.

Law of moments – when the total clockwise motion and total anticlockwise motion of an object are equal.

Liquid – state of matter where particles are less spread out than in a gas but more than in a solid.

Moment – a turning force; the product of the force and the perpendicular distance from the force to the pivot point.

Momentum – the fundamental quantity that is a measure of the state of motion of an object; product of mass and velocity; $p = m \times v$; units of kg m/s.

Noise – unwanted frequencies in a signal that can distort it.

Resultant force – the combined effect of all the forces acting on an object.

Scalar quantity – a quantity where there is only size.

Solid – a state of matter, where the particles are very close together.

Static electricity – build-up of charge on a substance.

Vector quantity – a quantity where both size and direction are known.

Average speed = $\dfrac{\text{Distance moved}}{\text{Time taken}}$	Moment = Force × Perpendicular distance from the pivot
Force = Mass × Acceleration	Charge = Current × Time
Acceleration = $\dfrac{\text{Change in velocity}}{\text{Time taken}}$	Voltage = Current × Resistance
Momentum = Mass × Velocity	Electrical power = Voltage × Current
Density = $\dfrac{\text{Mass}}{\text{Volume}}$	Wave speed = Frequency × Wavelength
Work done = Force × Distance moved	$\dfrac{\text{Input (primary) voltage}}{\text{Output (secondary) voltage}} = \dfrac{\text{Primary turns}}{\text{Secondary turns}}$
Energy transferred = Work done	$n = \dfrac{\sin i}{\sin r}$
Kinetic energy = $\dfrac{1}{2}$ × Mass × Speed²	$\sin c = \dfrac{1}{n}$
Gravitational potential energy = Mass × g × Height	Efficiency = $\dfrac{\text{Useful energy output}}{\text{Total energy output}}$
Weight = Mass × Gravitational Field Strength	Pressure difference = Height × density × g
Pressure = $\dfrac{\text{Force}}{\text{Area}}$	$V_p I_p = V_s I_s$ for 100% efficiency

Description	Symbol
Conductors crossing with no connection	
Junction of conductors	
Open switch	
Closed switch	
Open push switch	
Closed push switch	
Cell	
Battery of cells	
Power supply	(DC) or (AC)
Transformer	
Ammeter	A
Milliammeter	mA
Voltmeter	V
Fixed resistor	
Variable resistor	

Description	Symbol
Heater	
Thermistor	
Light-dependent resistor (LDR)	
Relay	
Diode	
Light-emitting diode (LED)	
Lamp	
Loudspeaker	
Microphone	
Electric bell	
Earth or ground	
Motor	M
Generator	G
Fuse/circuit breaker	

Index